California Maritime Academy Library (CSU)

3 0060 00062870 9

P9-DTB-496

NCEES
advancing licensure for
engineers and surveyors

FE

WITHDRAWN

mechanical
practice exam

Library
California Maritime Academy
200 Maritime Academy Dr.
Vallejo, CA 94590

978-1-932613-85-8

Copyright ©2017 by NCEES®. All rights reserved.

All NCEES sample questions and solutions are copyrighted under the laws of the United States. No part of this publication may be reproduced, stored in a retrieval system, or transmitted in any form or by any means without the prior written permission of NCEES. Requests for permissions should be addressed in writing to permissions@ncees.org or to NCEES Exam Publications, PO Box 1686, Clemson, SC 29633.

ISBN 978-1-932613-85-8

Printed in the United States of America
1st printing March 2017

CONTENTS

About NCEES

NCEES is a nonprofit organization made up of the U.S. engineering and surveying licensing boards in all 50 states, U.S. territories, and the District of Columbia. We develop and score the exams used for engineering and surveying licensure in the United States. NCEES also promotes professional mobility through its services for licensees and its member boards.

Engineering licensure in the United States is regulated by licensing boards in each state and territory. These boards set and maintain the standards that protect the public they serve. As a result, licensing requirements and procedures vary by jurisdiction, so stay in touch with your board (ncees.org/licensing-boards).

Exam Format

The FE exam contains 110 questions and is administered year-round via computer at approved Pearson VUE test centers. A 6-hour appointment time includes a tutorial, the exam, and a break. You'll have 5 hours and 20 minutes to complete the actual exam.

Beginning July 1, 2017, in addition to traditional multiple-choice questions with one correct answer, the FE exam will use common alternative item types such as

- Multiple correct options—allows multiple choices to be correct
- Point and click—requires examinees to click on part of a graphic to answer
- Drag and drop—requires examinees to click on and drag items to match, sort, rank, or label
- Fill in the blank—provides a space for examinees to enter a response to the question

To familiarize yourself with the format, style, and navigation of a computer-based exam, view the demo on ncees.org/ExamPrep.

Examinee Guide

The *NCEES Examinee Guide* is the official guide to policies and procedures for all NCEES exams. During exam registration and again on exam day, examinees must agree to abide by the conditions in the *Examinee Guide*, which includes the CBT Examinee Rules and Agreement. You can download the *Examinee Guide* at ncees.org/exams. It is your responsibility to make sure you have the current version.

Scoring and reporting

Exam results for computer-based exams are typically available 7–10 days after you take the exam. You will receive an email notification from NCEES with instructions to view your results in your MyNCEES account. All results are reported as pass or fail.

Updates on exam content and procedures

Visit us at **ncees.org/exams** for updates on everything exam-related, including specifications, exam-day policies, scoring, and corrections to published exam preparation materials. This is also where you will register for the exam and find additional steps you should follow in your state to be approved for the exam.

Fundamentals of Engineering (FE)
MECHANICAL CBT Exam Specifications
Effective Beginning with the January 2014 Examinations

- The FE exam is a computer-based test (CBT). It is closed book with an electronic reference.

- Examinees have 6 hours to complete the exam, which contains 110 multiple-choice questions. The 6-hour time also includes a tutorial and an optional scheduled break.

- The FE exam uses both the International System of Units (SI) and the U.S. Customary System (USCS).

Knowledge	Number of Questions
1. Mathematics A. Analytic geometry B. Calculus C. Linear algebra D. Vector analysis E. Differential equations F. Numerical methods	6–9
2. Probability and Statistics A. Probability distributions B. Regression and curve fitting	4–6
3. Computational Tools A. Spreadsheets B. Flow charts	3–5
4. Ethics and Professional Practice A. Codes of ethics B. Agreements and contracts C. Ethical and legal considerations D. Professional liability E. Public health, safety, and welfare	3–5
5. Engineering Economics A. Time value of money B. Cost, including incremental, average, sunk, and estimating C. Economic analyses D. Depreciation	3–5

6. **Electricity and Magnetism**   3–5
   A. Charge, current, voltage, power, and energy
   B. Current and voltage laws (Kirchhoff, Ohm)
   C. Equivalent circuits (series, parallel)
   D. AC circuits
   E. Motors and generators

7. **Statics**   8–12
   A. Resultants of force systems
   B. Concurrent force systems
   C. Equilibrium of rigid bodies
   D. Frames and trusses
   E. Centroids
   F. Moments of inertia
   G. Static friction

8. **Dynamics, Kinematics, and Vibrations**   9–14
   A. Kinematics of particles
   B. Kinetic friction
   C. Newton's second law for particles
   D. Work-energy of particles
   E. Impulse-momentum of particles
   F. Kinematics of rigid bodies
   G. Kinematics of mechanisms
   H. Newton's second law for rigid bodies
   I. Work-energy of rigid bodies
   J. Impulse-momentum of rigid bodies
   K. Free and forced vibrations

9. **Mechanics of Materials**   8–12
   A. Shear and moment diagrams
   B. Stress types (axial, bending, torsion, shear)
   C. Stress transformations
   D. Mohr's circle
   E. Stress and strain caused by axial loads
   F. Stress and strain caused by bending loads
   G. Stress and strain caused by torsion
   H. Stress and strain caused by shear
   I. Combined loading
   J. Deformations
   K. Columns

10. **Material Properties and Processing**   8–12
    A. Properties, including chemical, electrical, mechanical, physical, and thermal
    B. Stress-strain diagrams
    C. Engineered materials
    D. Ferrous metals
    E. Nonferrous metals
    F. Manufacturing processes
    G. Phase diagrams
    H. Phase transformation, equilibrium, and heat treating
    I. Materials selection
    J. Surface conditions
    K. Corrosion mechanisms and control
    L. Thermal failure
    M. Ductile or brittle behavior
    N. Fatigue
    O. Crack propagation

11. **Fluid Mechanics**   9–14
    A. Fluid properties
    B. Fluid statics
    C. Energy, impulse, and momentum
    D. Internal flow
    E. External flow
    F. Incompressible flow
    G. Compressible flow
    H. Power and efficiency
    I. Performance curves
    J. Scaling laws for fans, pumps, and compressors

12. **Thermodynamics**   13–20
    A. Properties of ideal gases and pure substances
    B. Energy transfers
    C. Laws of thermodynamics
    D. Processes
    E. Performance of components
    F. Power cycles, thermal efficiency, and enhancements
    G. Refrigeration and heat pump cycles and coefficients of performance
    H. Nonreacting mixtures of gases
    I. Psychrometrics
    J. Heating, ventilating, and air-conditioning (HVAC) processes
    K. Combustion and combustion products

1. The equation of a sphere with center at $(0, 1, -2)$ and a radius of 9 is:

    A. $x^2 + (y - 1)^2 + (z + 2)^2 = 81$
    B. $x^2 + (y + 1)^2 + (z - 2)^2 = 81$
    C. $(x + 1)^2 + (y + 1)^2 + (z + 2)^2 = 81$
    D. $(x)^2 + (y - 1)^2 + (z + 2)^2 = 9$

2. The area of the shaded portion of the figure shown below is most nearly:

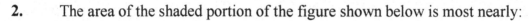

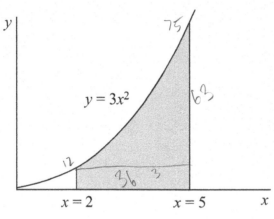

$y = 3x^2$

$x = 2$ $x = 5$

    A. 18
    B. 39
    C. 117
    D. 133

Copyright © 2017 by NCEES

NEXT→

3.   What is the area of the region in the first quadrant that is bounded by the line $y = 1$, the curve $x = y^{3/2}$, and the y-axis?

○ A.   2/5

○ B.   3/5

○ C.   2/3

○ D.   1

4.   Which of the following is a unit vector perpendicular to the plane determined by the vectors $\mathbf{A} = 2\mathbf{i} + 4\mathbf{j}$ and $\mathbf{B} = \mathbf{i} + \mathbf{j} - \mathbf{k}$?

$$\begin{vmatrix} \mathbf{i} & \mathbf{j} & \mathbf{k} \\ 2 & 4 & 0 \\ 1 & 1 & -1 \end{vmatrix} \quad -4\mathbf{i} + 2\mathbf{j} - 2\mathbf{k}$$

○ A. $-2\mathbf{i} + \mathbf{j} - \mathbf{k}$

○ B. $\dfrac{1}{\sqrt{5}}(\mathbf{i} + 2\mathbf{j})$

○ C. $\dfrac{1}{\sqrt{6}}(-2\mathbf{i} + \mathbf{j} - \mathbf{k})$

○ D. $\dfrac{1}{\sqrt{6}}(-2\mathbf{i} - \mathbf{j} - \mathbf{k})$

5. Suppose $f(t) = t^2$. The area under the curve for $0 \leq t \leq 2$, estimated by using the trapezoidal rule with $\Delta t = 0.5$, is most nearly:

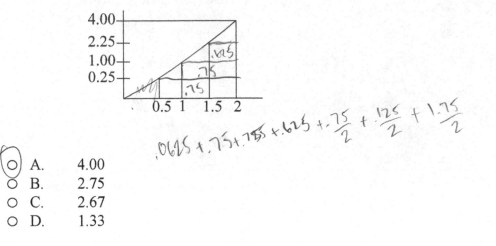

$.0625 + .75 + .75 + .625 + \frac{.75}{2} + \frac{.125}{2} + \frac{1.75}{2}$

- A. 4.00
- B. 2.75
- C. 2.67
- D. 1.33

6. A series of measurements gave values of 11, 11, 11, 11, 12, 13, 13, 14, for which the arithmetic mean is 12. The population standard deviation is most nearly:

- A. 1.42
- B. 1.25
- C. 1.19
- D. 1.12

7. Suppose the lengths of telephone calls form a normal distribution with a mean length of 8.0 min and a standard deviation of 2.5 min. The probability that a telephone call selected at random will last more than 15.5 min is most nearly:

- A. 0.0013
- B. 0.0026
- C. 0.2600
- D. 0.9987

8. You wish to estimate the mean M of a population from a sample of size n drawn from the population. For the sample, the mean is x and the standard deviation is s. The probable accuracy of the estimate improves with an increase in:

- A. M
- B. n
- C. s
- D. $M + s$

9. Consider a set of three values: 4, 4, and 7.

Match each of the statistical quantities with the correct value.

Statistical Quantities

Mean ___5___   2/3

2   3

Variance _3_

4   5

Median _4_

6   7

10. A spreadsheet display shows the following values in Column A:

	A	B
1	–2	
2	–1	
3	0	
4	1	
5	2	

Cell B1 contains the formula $A1^3 + A$1^2 – 3. The formula in Cell B1 is copied down in Column B with automatic cell referencing. The formula in Cell B5 will be:

- A. $A1^3 + A$5^2 – 3
- B. A5^3 + B$1^2 – 3
- C. $A5^3 + A$1^2 – 3
- D. A5^3 + A5^2 – 3

11. In a spreadsheet, the number in Cell A4 is set to 6. Then A5 is set to A4 + A4. This formula is copied into Cells A6 and A7 with automatic cell referencing. The number shown in Cell A7 is most nearly:

A. 12
B. 24
C. 36
D. 216

(handwritten: 5 12 / 6 18 / 7)

12. The flowchart for a computer program contains the following segment:

```
VAR = 0
IF VAR < 5 THEN VAR = VAR + 2
OTHERWISE EXIT LOOP
LOOP
```

What is the value of VAR at the conclusion of this routine?

A. 0
B. 2
C. 4
D. 6

13. The final value of Q in the following flowchart is most nearly:

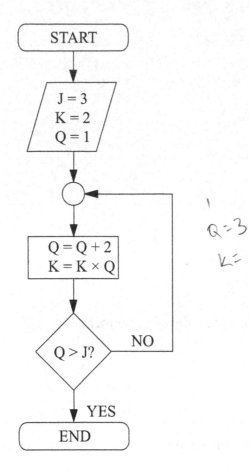

- ○ A. 0
- ○ B. 1
- ○ C. 3
- ⊘ D. 5

14. According to the *Model Rules*, Section 240.15, Rules of Professional Conduct, licensed professional engineers are obligated to:

   ○ A. ensure that design documents and surveys are reviewed by a panel of licensed engineers prior to affixing a seal of approval

   ⊗ B. express public opinions under the direction of an employer or client regardless of knowledge of subject matter

   ○ C. practice by performing services only in the areas of their competence and in accordance with the current standards of technical competence

   ⊗ D. offer, give, or solicit services directly or indirectly in order to secure work or other valuable or political considerations

15. As a professional engineer originally licensed 30 years ago, you are asked to evaluate a newly developed computerized control system for a public transportation system. The owner requires a currently licensed engineer to evaluate the system. You may accept this project if:

   ○ A. you are competent in the area of modern control systems

   ⊗ B. your professional engineering license has lapsed, but you have two FE interns working for you

   ⊗ C. you took a transportation course in college

   ○ D. you have regularly attended meetings of a professional engineering society

16. Which of the following is the general solution to the differential equation and boundary condition shown below?

$$\frac{dy}{dt} + 5y = 0; \, y(0) = 1$$

○ A. e^{5t} $5e^{5x} \stackrel{?}{=}$
⊙ B. e^{-5t} $5e^{5x}$
○ C. $e^{\sqrt{-5t}}$ $5e$
○ D. $5e^{-5t}$

17. A printer costs $900. Its salvage value after 5 years is $300. Annual maintenance is $50. If the interest rate is 8%, the equivalent uniform annual cost is _____.

Answer to the nearest integer. $206

$$\frac{600}{5}$$

$$120 + 50$$

$$198.20$$

FE MECHANICAL PRACTICE EXAM

18. Economic analysis will be used to compute an equivalent value today for an estimated constant monthly expense that is projected to occur each month over the next three years.

Mark the area of the single column of the factor table that contains the value that could be used for such an analysis.

Factor Table –$i = 2.00\%$

n	P/F	P/A	P/G	F/P	F/A	A/P	A/F	A/G
1	0.9804	0.9804	0.0000	1.0200	1.0000	1.0200	1.0000	0.0000
2	0.9612	1.9416	0.9612	1.0404	2.0200	0.5150	0.4950	0.4950
3	0.9423	2.8839	2.8458	1.0612	3.0604	0.3468	0.3268	0.9868
4	0.9238	3.8077	5.6173	1.0824	4.1216	0.2626	0.2426	1.4752
5	0.9057	4.7135	9.2403	1.1041	5.2040	0.2122	0.1922	1.9604
6	0.8880	5.6014	13.6801	1.1262	6.3081	0.1785	0.1585	2.4423
7	0.8706	6.4720	18.9035	1.1487	7.4343	0.1545	0.1345	2.9208
8	0.8535	7.3255	24.8779	1.1717	8.5830	0.1365	0.1165	3.3961
9	0.8368	8.1622	31.5720	1.1951	9.7546	0.1225	0.1025	3.8681
10	0.8203	8.9826	38.9551	1.2190	10.9497	0.1113	0.0913	4.3367
11	0.8043	9.7868	46.9977	1.2434	12.1687	0.1022	0.0822	4.8021
12	0.7885	10.5753	55.6712	1.2682	13.4121	0.0946	0.0746	5.2642
13	0.7730	11.3484	64.9475	1.2936	14.6803	0.0881	0.0681	5.7231
14	0.7579	12.1062	74.7999	1.3195	15.9739	0.0826	0.0626	6.1786
15	0.7430	12.8493	85.2021	1.3459	17.2934	0.0778	0.0578	6.6309
16	0.7284	13.5777	96.1288	1.3728	18.6393	0.0737	0.0537	7.0799
17	0.7142	14.2919	107.5554	1.4002	20.0121	0.0700	0.0500	7.5256
18	0.7002	14.9920	119.4581	1.4282	21.4123	0.0677	0.0467	7.9681
19	0.6864	15.6785	131.8139	1.4568	22.8406	0.0638	0.0438	8.4073
20	0.6730	16.3514	144.6003	1.4859	24.2974	0.0612	0.0412	8.8433
21	0.6598	17.0112	157.7959	1.5157	25.7833	0.0588	0.0388	9.2760
22	0.6468	17.6580	171.3795	1.5460	27.2990	0.0566	0.0366	9.7055
23	0.6342	18.2922	185.3309	1.5769	28.8450	0.0547	0.0347	10.1317
24	0.6217	18.9139	199.6305	1.6084	30.4219	0.0529	0.0329	10.5547
25	0.6095	19.5235	214.2592	1.6406	32.0303	0.0512	0.0312	10.9745
30	0.5521	22.3965	291.7164	1.8114	40.5681	0.0446	0.0246	13.0251
40	0.4529	27.3555	461.9931	2.2080	60.4020	0.0366	0.0166	16.8885
50	0.3715	31.4236	642.3606	2.6916	84.5794	0.0318	0.0118	20.4420
60	0.3048	34.7609	823.6975	3.2810	114.0515	0.0288	0.0088	23.6961
100	0.1380	43.0984	1,464.7527	7.2446	312.2323	0.0232	0.0032	33.9863

19. The power (W) dissipated in the 90-Ω resistor of the circuit shown below is most nearly:

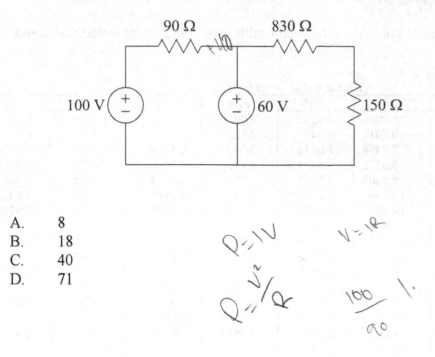

- ○ A. 8
- ○ B. 18
- ○ C. 40
- ○ D. 71

$P = IV$

$V = IR$

$P = \frac{V^2}{R}$

$\frac{100}{90} \cdot 1.$

20. In the resistor circuit shown below, the equivalent resistance R_{eq} (Ω) at Terminals a-b is most nearly:

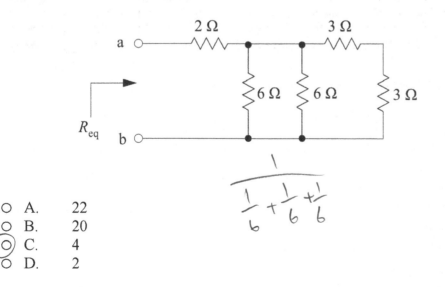

- ○ A. 22
- ○ B. 20
- ○ C. 4
- ○ D. 2

$\dfrac{1}{\frac{1}{6} + \frac{1}{6} + \frac{1}{6}}$

21. A 1,000-Ω resistor is in series with a 2-mH inductor. An ac voltage source operating at a frequency of 100,000 rad/s is attached as shown in the figure. The impedance (Ω) of the *RL* combination is most nearly:

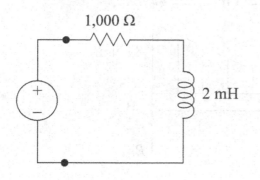

1,000 Ω

2 mH

A. $200 + j1,000$
B. $1,000 + j200$
C. $38.4 + j192$
D. $1,000 - j200$

$Z = R + jX \Rightarrow X = \omega L$

$100,000(.002)$

22. An ammeter, a voltmeter, and a wattmeter were installed in an ac circuit and read 15 A_{rms}, 115 V_{rms}, and 1,500 W, respectively. The power factor of the circuit is most nearly:

A. -0.87
B. -0.5
C. 0.5
D. 0.87

$P = V_{rms}(I_{rms}) \cos\theta$

$\cos^{-1}\left(\frac{P}{V_{rms} I_{rms}}\right) = 0.51$

23. Beam AB has a distributed load as shown and supports at A and B. If the weight of the beam is negligible, the force R_B (kN) is most nearly:

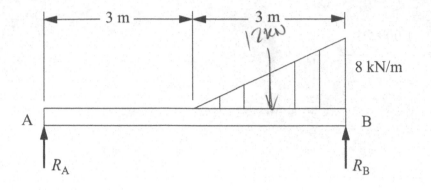

O A.   24
O B.   12
O C.   10
O D.   8

$$M_A = 0$$

$$0 = -12(4.5m) + R_B(6)$$

24. Three forces act as shown below. The magnitude (N) of the resultant of the three forces is most nearly:

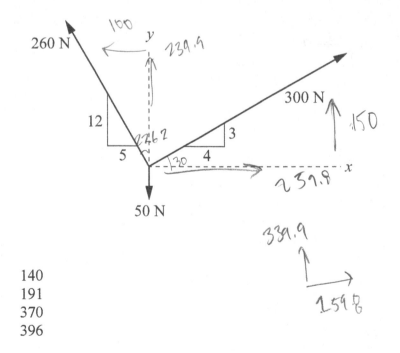

O A.   140
O B.   191
O C.   370
O D.   396

25. The moment of force **F** (N·m) shown below with respect to Point P is most nearly:

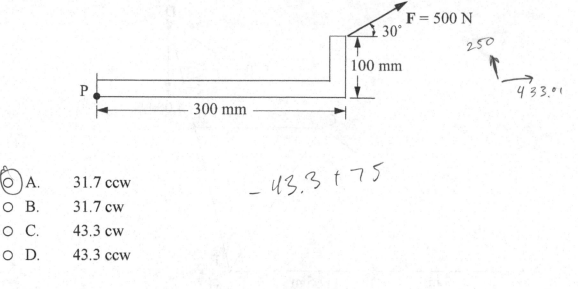

- A. 31.7 ccw
- B. 31.7 cw
- C. 43.3 cw
- D. 43.3 ccw

26. In the figure below, the force (kN) in Member BC is most nearly:

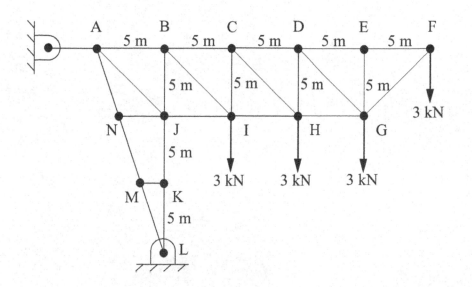

- A. 6
- B. 9
- C. 15
- D. 18

27. Mark all of the zero-force members of the simple truss below.

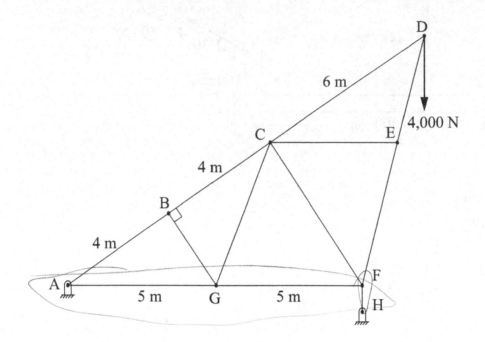

28. Consider the following graph:

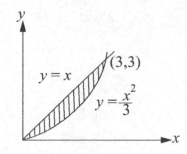

Which of the following expressions gives the distance from the y-axis to the centroid of the shaded area?

O A. $\dfrac{\int_0^3 \frac{1}{3}x^3\,dx}{\int_0^3\left(x+\frac{1}{3}x^2\right)dx}$

O B. $\dfrac{\int_0^3\left(x^2-\frac{1}{3}x^3\right)dx}{\int_0^3\left(x-\frac{1}{3}x^2\right)dx}$

O C. $\dfrac{\int_0^3\left(x-\frac{1}{3}x^2\right)dx}{\int_0^3\left(x-\frac{1}{3}x^2\right)dx}$

O D. $\dfrac{\int_0^3\left(\frac{1}{2}x^2+\frac{1}{3}x^3\right)dx}{\int_0^3\left(x-\frac{1}{3}x^2\right)dx}$

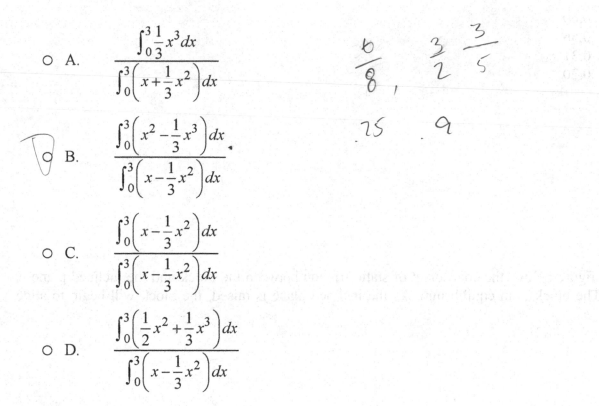

29. A pulley is driven by a belt as shown in the figure below. Neglecting centrifugal effects, the minimum coefficient of friction that will prevent slipping between the belt and the pulley is most nearly:

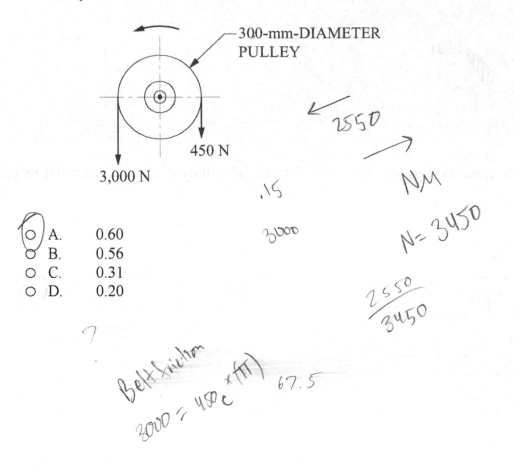

A. 0.60
B. 0.56
C. 0.31
D. 0.20

30. In the figure below, the coefficient of static friction between the block and the inclined plane is 0.25. The block is in equilibrium. As the inclined plane is raised, the block will begin to slide when:

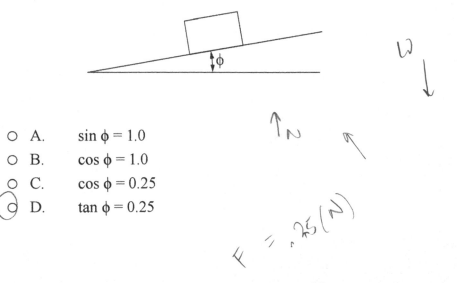

A. $\sin \phi = 1.0$
B. $\cos \phi = 1.0$
C. $\cos \phi = 0.25$
D. $\tan \phi = 0.25$

31. Two blocks, A and B, are arranged so that A rests on top of B and is attached to a vertical wall by an inextensible string. A force of 30 N is applied to Block B, which is sufficient to make it slide to the left. If $\mu_K = 0.2$ between A and B, and if $\mu_K = 0.4$ between B and the bottom surface, the acceleration of B (m/s^2) is most nearly:

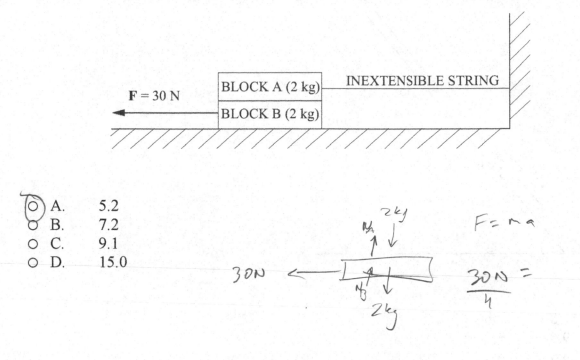

- A.   5.2
- B.   7.2
- C.   9.1
- D.   15.0

32. A 2-kg block slides along a rough horizontal surface and slows to 10 m/s after traveling 20 m. If the kinetic coefficient of friction between the block and surface is 0.2, the initial speed (m/s) of the block was most nearly:

- A.   10.0
- B.   10.4
- C.   13.4
- D.   20.0

33. The 2-kg block shown in the figure is accelerated from rest by force **F** along the smooth incline for 5 m until it clears the top of the ramp at a speed of 8 m/s. The value of **F** (N) is most nearly:

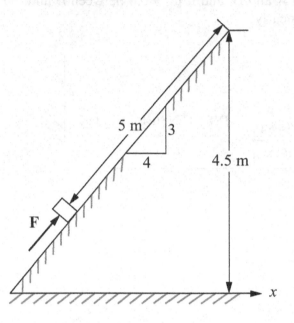

- ○ A.   11.8
- ○ B.   19.6
- ○ C.   24.6
- ○ D.   69.4

$F = ma$

Copyright © 2017 by NCEES

34. The piston and cylinder of an internal combustion engine are shown in the following figure. If $\omega = 377$ rad/s, the piston speed (mm/s) when $\theta = 90°$ is most nearly:

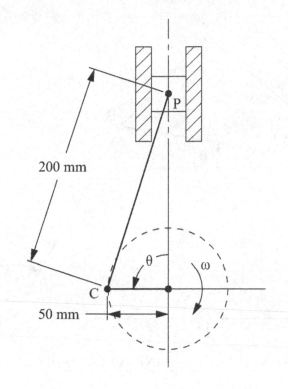

- A. 0
- B. 10,500
- C. 18,850
- D. 24,300

35. The figure shows a four-bar linkage. If Link 3 rotates in the counterclockwise direction, the angle at Point P, measured in the global X-Y coordinate frame, is most nearly:

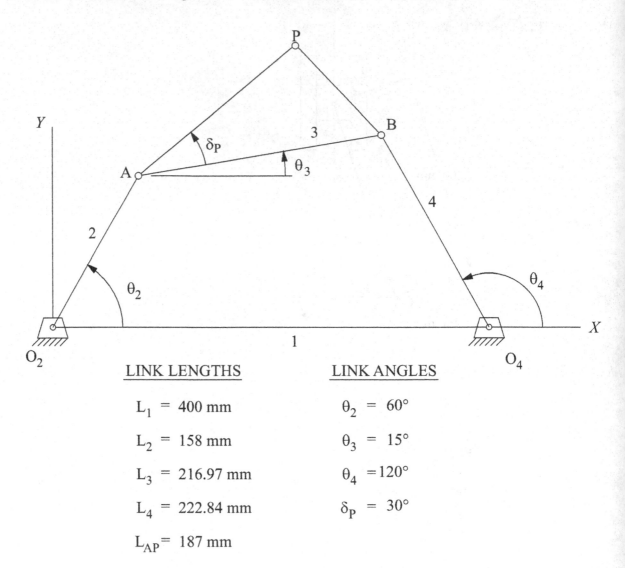

LINK LENGTHS	LINK ANGLES
L_1 = 400 mm	θ_2 = 60°
L_2 = 158 mm	θ_3 = 15°
L_3 = 216.97 mm	θ_4 = 120°
L_4 = 222.84 mm	δ_P = 30°
L_{AP} = 187 mm	

- ○ A.   225°
- ⊚ B.   135°
- ○ C.   45°
- ○ D.   −45°

36. An object with a mass *m* of 1.50 kg moves without friction in a circular path as shown below. Attached to the object is a spring with a spring constant *k* of 400 N/m. The spring is undeformed when the object is at Point P, and the speed of the object at Point Q is 2.00 m/s.

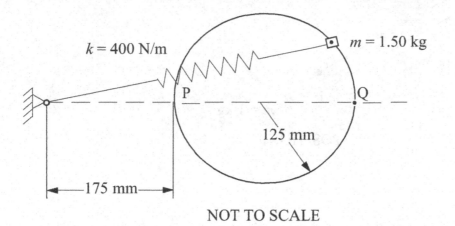

$k = 400$ N/m

$m = 1.50$ kg

P

Q

125 mm

175 mm

NOT TO SCALE

The translational kinetic energy (J) of the object at Point Q is most nearly:

- A. 1.50
- B. 3.00
- C. 6.00
- D. 29.40

Copyright © 2017 by NCEES
NEXT→

37. If a pendulum is released from rest at Position 1, the velocity (m/s) of the mass at Position 2 is most nearly:

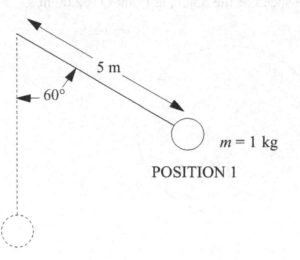

POSITION 1

POSITION 2

- A. 5.0
- B. 7.0
- C. 9.8
- D. 12.7

38. In the figure below, Block B is initially at rest and is attached to an unstretched spring. Block A travels to the right and hits Block B. Immediately after impact, the velocity of Block B is 6 m/s to the right. The maximum acceleration (m/s²) of Block B after impact is most nearly:

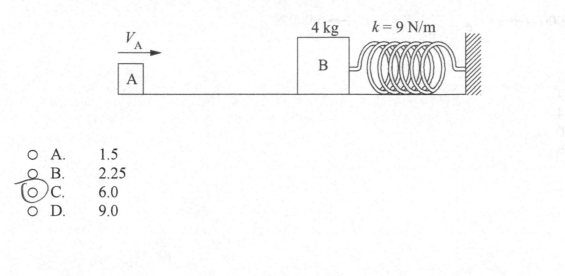

- O A.   1.5
- O B.   2.25
- ⊙ C.   6.0
- O D.   9.0

39. The shear diagram for a particular beam is shown below. All lines in the diagram are straight. The bending moment at each end of the beam is zero, and there are no concentrated couples along the beam. The maximum magnitude of the bending moment (kN·m) in the beam is most nearly:

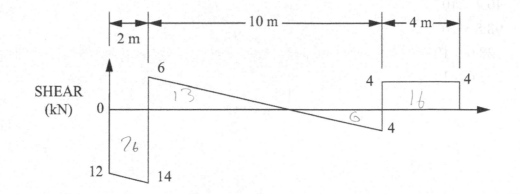

- O A.   8
- O B.   16
- O C.   18
- ⊙ D.   26

40. A 0.25-m steel rod with a cross-sectional area of 1,250 mm^2 and a modulus of elasticity E of 200 GPa is subjected to a 5,000-N force as shown below. The elongation of the rod (μm) is most nearly:

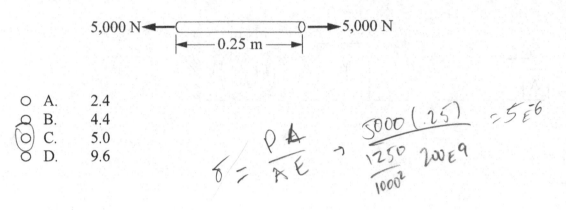

5,000 N ← ⊂——————⊃ → 5,000 N

|← 0.25 m →|

- ○ A. 2.4
- ○ B. 4.4
- Ⓒ C. 5.0
- ○ D. 9.6

$$\delta = \frac{PA}{AE} \rightarrow \frac{5000\,(.25)}{\frac{1250}{1000^2}\,200E9} = 5\bar{E}6$$

41. The piston of a steam engine is 50 cm in diameter, and the maximum steam gage pressure is 1.4 MPa. If the design stress for the piston rod is 68 MPa, its cross-sectional area (m^2) should be most nearly:

- ○ A. 40.4×10^{-4}
- ○ B. 98.8×10^{-4}
- Ⓒ C. 228.0×10^{-4}
- ○ D. 323.0×10^{-4}

42. In the figure below, the value of the maximum shear stress (MPa) in Segment BC is most nearly:

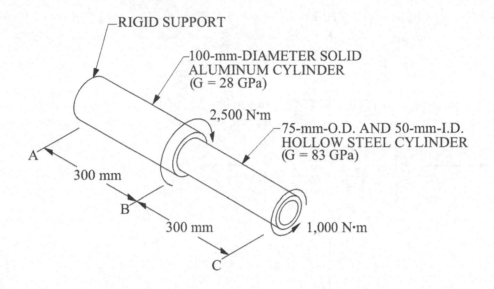

- A. 15.0
- B. 30.0
- C. 37.7
- D. 52.7

43. A shaft of wood is to be used in a certain process. If the allowable shearing stress parallel to the grain of the wood is 840 kN/m^2, the torque (N·m) transmitted by a 200-mm-diameter shaft with the grain parallel to the neutral axis is most nearly:

- A. 500
- B. 1,200
- C. 1,320
- D. 1,500

44. The maximum inplane shear stress (ksi) in the element shown below is most nearly:

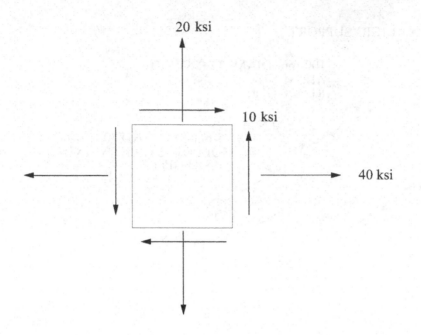

- A. 10
- B. 14.1
- C. 44.1
- D. 316

$T_{in} = R$

$$R = \sqrt{\left(\frac{40-20}{2}\right)^2 + 10}$$

Copyright © 2017 by NCEES

NEXT→

45. A plane member having a uniform thickness of 10 mm is loaded as shown below. The maximum shear stress (MPa) at Point O is most nearly:

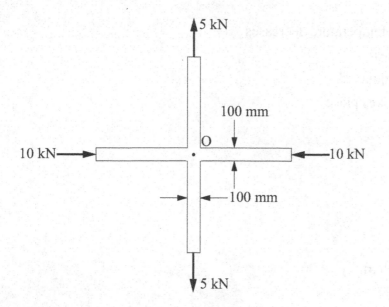

- ○ A. 2.5
- ○ B. 5.0
- ○ C. 7.5
- ○ D. 10.0

46. The Euler formula for columns deals with:

- ○ A. relatively short columns
- ○ B. shear stress
- ○ C. tensile stress
- ○ D. elastic buckling

47.   When a metal is cold-worked, all of the following generally occur **except**:

     ○ A.   recrystallization temperature decreases

     ○ B.   ductility decreases

     ○ C.   grains become equiaxed

     ○ D.   slip or twining takes place

48.   Refer to the following chart:

Constants for Diffusivity			
Solute	Solvent	D_o (m^2/s)	Q (J/mol)
Carbon	FCC Iron	0.2×10^{-4}	142,350
Carbon	BCC Iron	2.2×10^{-4}	122,673
Nickel	FCC Iron	0.77×10^{-4}	280,516
Copper	Aluminum	0.15×10^{-4}	126,441
Copper	Copper	0.2×10^{-4}	197,198
Carbon	HCP Titanium	5.1×10^{-4}	182,126

The temperature at which carbon has the same diffusivity in FCC iron as it has in HCP titanium is most nearly:

     ○ A.   1,200°C

     ○ B.   1,500°C

     ○ C.   8,200°C

     ○ D.   8,500°C

49. The mechanical deformation of a material above its recrystallization temperature is commonly known as:

- ○ A.   hot working
- ○ B.   strain aging
- ○ C.   grain growth
- ○ D.   cold working

50.   The silver/copper binary phase diagram is shown below. The composition of Ag-Cu alloy that will be completely melted at the lowest temperature is most nearly:

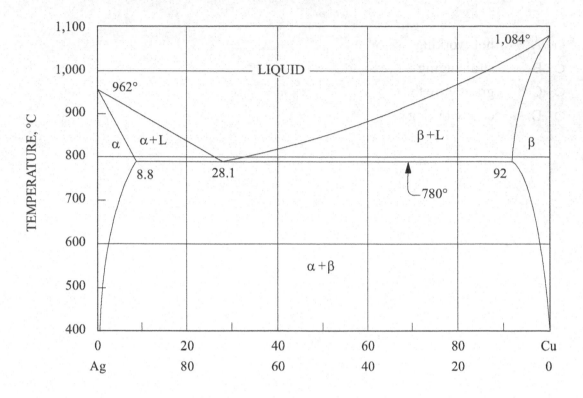

COMPOSITION, % BY WEIGHT

- ○ A.   8.0 wt% Cu
- ○ B.   8.8 wt% Cu
- ○ C.   28.1 wt% Cu
- ○ D.   71.9 wt% Cu

51. An alloy that is 70% copper by weight is fully melted and allowed to cool slowly. What phases are present at 850°C?

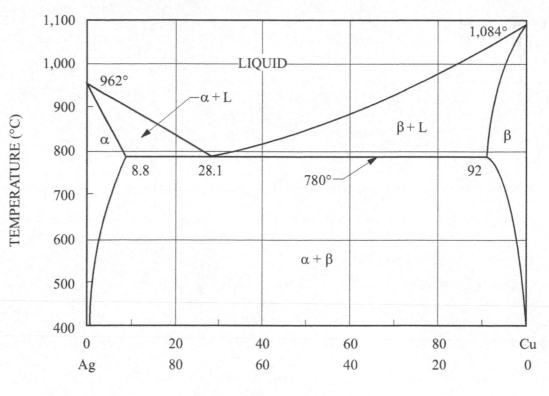

- ○ A. Liquid only
- ○ B. $\alpha + \beta$
- ○ C. $\alpha + L$
- ○ D. $\beta + L$

52.   A 40-mm-diameter bar made of 4140 steel is quenched in an agitated oil bath. The expected R_c hardness of the center of the bar is most nearly:

     ○ A.   54
     ○ B.   52
     ○ C.   49
     ○ D.   42

53.   If an aluminum crimp connector were used to connect a copper wire to a battery, what would you expect to happen?

     ○ A.   Only the copper wire will corrode.

     ○ B.   Only the aluminum connector will corrode.

     ○ C.   Both will corrode.

     ○ D.   Nothing

54. A part is to be formed by bending a thick sheet of Al 2024-T3, which has the following properties:

Fracture toughness = 44 MPa·m$^{1/2}$
Yield strength = 345 MPa

The critical length (mm) of an exterior crack that can be tolerated in the as-received sheet is most nearly:

- ○ A.   2.2
- ○ B.   4.3
- ○ C.   6.9
- ○ D.   13

55. A fluid has a specific gravity of 1.263 and an absolute dynamic viscosity of 1.5 kg/(m·s). The standard density of water is 1,000 kg/m^3. The kinematic viscosity (m^2/s) of the fluid is most nearly:

- ○ A. 1.19×10^{-3}
- ○ B. 1.50×10^{-3}
- ○ C. 1.89×10^{-3}
- ○ D.   528

56. Which of the following statements is true of viscosity?

    ○ A.   It is the ratio of inertial to viscous force.

    ○ B.   It always has a large effect on the value of the friction factor.

    ○ C.   It is the ratio of the shear stress to the rate of shear deformation.

    ○ D.   It is usually low when turbulent forces predominate.

57. Archimedes' principle states that:

    ○ A.   the sum of the pressure, velocity, and elevation heads is constant

    ○ B.   flow passing two points in a stream is equal at each point

    ○ C.   the buoyant force on a body is equal to the volume displaced by the body

    ○ D.   a floating body displaces a weight of fluid equal to its own weight

58. The rectangular, homogeneous gate shown below is 3.00 m high × 1.00 m wide and has a frictionless hinge at the bottom. If the fluid on the left side of the gate has a density of 1,600 kg/m³, the magnitude of the force **F** (kN) required to keep the gate closed is most nearly:

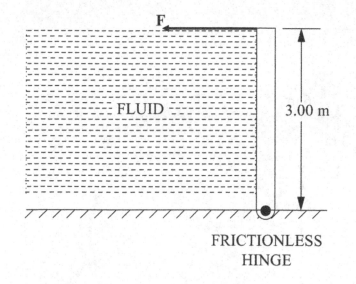

- ○ A.   0
- ○ B.   22
- ○ C.   24
- ○ D.   220

59. Water is discharged to the atmosphere as a jet from a puncture in the bottom of a ventilated storage tank. The storage tank is a cylinder 6 m high mounted on a level platform 2 m off the ground. If losses are neglected, the jet velocity (m/s) when the tank is half full is most nearly:

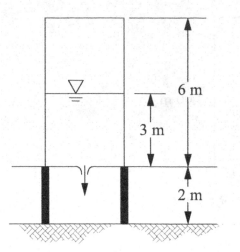

- ○ A. 7.7
- ○ B. 9.9
- ○ C. 12.5
- ○ D. 50.8

60. A horizontal jet of water (density = 1,000 kg/m³) is deflected perpendicularly to the original jet stream by a plate as shown below. The magnitude of force **F** (kN) required to hold the plate in place is most nearly:

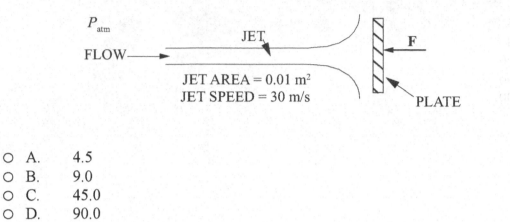

- A. 4.5
- B. 9.0
- C. 45.0
- D. 90.0

61. The mass flow rate of sodium traveling through a pipe with an inside diameter of 0.1023 m is 22.7 kg/s. The mass density of the sodium is 823.3 kg/m³, and the dynamic viscosity is 2.32×10^{-4} kg/(m·s). The Reynolds number for sodium flow through the pipe is most nearly:

- A. 10,000
- B. 100,000
- C. 1,000,000
- D. 1,200,000

62. The density of water is 898 kg/m^3. The dynamic viscosity is $1.59 \times 10^{-4} \text{ N} \cdot \text{s/m}^2$. The Reynolds number for the water flowing at 1.5 m/s inside 3-m-long tubes with an inner diameter of 2.5 cm is most nearly:

- A. 53,000
- B. 106,000
- C. 212,000
- D. 424,000

63. For the system shown, the pipe is steel with an internal diameter of 100 mm. Water is pumped through the system; its velocity at Point C is 2.5 m/s. The pressure at Point A is atmospheric, the gage pressure at Point B is 125 kPa, and the gage pressure at Point C is 175 kPa. The discharge at Point D is to the atmosphere. The pumping rate (m³/min) is most nearly:

Viscosity, $\mu = 1.0 \times 10^{-3}$ N·s/m²
Kinematic viscosity, $v = 1.0 \times 10^{-6}$ m²/s
Density, $\rho = 1,000$ kg/m³

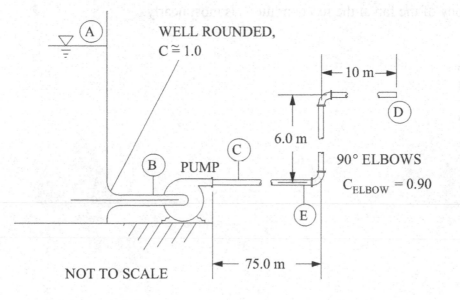

- A.   1.02
- B.   1.18
- C.   1.50
- D.   4.71

64. The following data were obtained from a test on a centrifugal fan:

> Fluid = Air at 300 K, 101 kPa
> Fan wheel diameter = 0.5 m
> Speed = 1,000 rpm
> Flow rate = 3.0 m³/s
> Pressure rise = 0.90 kPa
> Power = 4.0 kW

The efficiency of the fan at the test conditions is most nearly:

- A. 0.38
- B. 0.53
- C. 0.68
- D. 0.82

65. The pressure of 100 kg of nitrogen (N_2) at 70°C in a 100-m³ tank is most nearly:

- A. 2,850 kPa
- B. 102 kPa
- C. 20 kPa
- D. 102 mPa

66.   An insulated tank contains half liquid and half vapor by volume in equilibrium. The release of a small quantity of the vapor without the addition of heat will cause:

○ A.   evaporation of some liquid in the tank
○ B.   superheating of the vapor in the tank
○ C.   a rise in temperature
○ D.   an increase in enthalpy

67.   One kilogram of air, an ideal gas, is at 172 kPa and 100°C. The specific volume of the air (m^3/kg) is most nearly:

○ A.   0.17
○ B.   0.62
○ C.   0.93
○ D.   1.28

68. A power plant operates on the following simple Rankine cycle. Water is the working fluid. Disregard pressure losses in the piping, steam boiler, and superheater, and neglect kinetic and potential energy effects. Assume steady-state, steady-flow conditions.

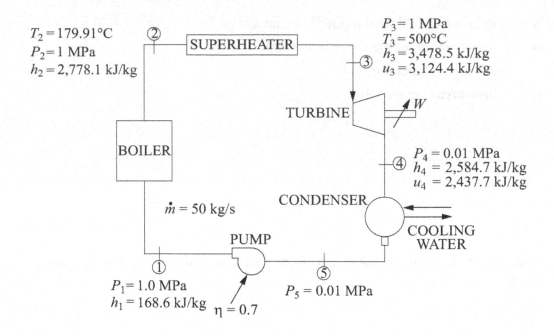

For the thermodynamic conditions shown, the turbine power (MW) is most nearly:

- A.   34.3
- B.   44.7
- C.   52.0
- D.   161,000

69. The pump shown in the figure is used to pump 50,000 kg of water per hour into a boiler. Pump discharge conditions are 40°C and 14.0 MPa. Boiler outlet conditions are 500°C and 14.0 MPa.

P (MPa)	T (°C)	Condition	h (kJ/kg)
14.0	40	Compressed liquid	167.6
14.0	500	Superheated vapor	3,322

The rate of heat transfer (MW) to the working fluid that occurs in the boiler is most nearly:

- A. 10
- B. 15
- C. 29
- D. 44

70. Which of the following statements about flow through an insulated valve are most accurate?

Select **all** that apply.

- A. The enthalpy rises.
- B. The upstream and downstream enthalpies are equal.
- C. Pressure increases sharply.
- D. Temperature increases sharply.
- E. There is no heat transfer.

71. A power plant operates on the following simple Rankine cycle. Water is the working fluid. Disregard pressure losses in the piping, steam boiler, and superheater, and neglect kinetic and potential energy effects. Assume steady-state, steady-flow conditions.

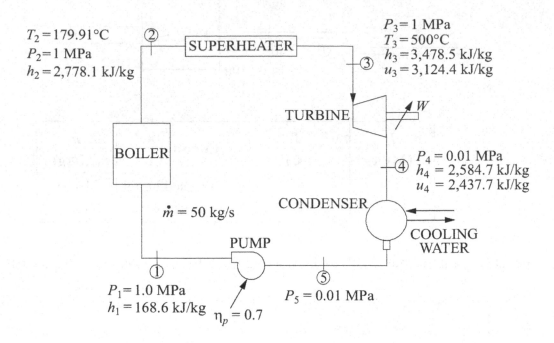

If the pump isentropic efficiency is 70%, the power (kW) required to drive the pump is most nearly:

- A. 0.70
- B. 1.43
- C. 35.0
- D. 71.0

72. The enthalpies provided in the figure below apply to the refrigeration cycle using refrigerant HFC-134a. The coefficient of performance (COP) for this cycle is most nearly:

$$h_1 = 394 \text{ kJ/kg}$$
$$h_2 = 438 \text{ kJ/kg}$$
$$h_3 = 270 \text{ kJ/kg}$$

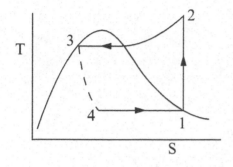

- ○ A.   0.35
- ○ B.   2.82
- ○ C.   3.82
- ○ D.   Cannot be determined from data given

73. A vapor-compression refrigeration cycle using HFC-134a as the refrigerant has the pressure-enthalpy diagram shown below. The evaporator temperature is 0°C, and the condenser temperature is 40°C.

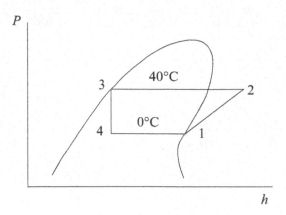

The cooling achieved by the evaporator (kJ/kg) is most nearly:

- A. 28
- B. 143
- C. 169
- D. 210

74. A vapor-compression refrigeration cycle using HFC-134a as the refrigerant has the pressure-enthalpy diagram shown below. The evaporator temperature is 0°C, and the condenser temperature is 40°C.

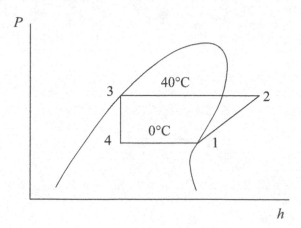

The process 3–4 is:

- ○ A.   constant entropy
- ○ B.   constant enthalpy
- ○ C.   reversible
- ○ D.   both constant entropy and enthalpy

75. Conditioned air enters a room at 13°C and 70% relative humidity. The dew-point temperature of the air is most nearly:

○ A.   5°C
○ B.   8°C
○ C.   10°C
○ D.   13°C

76. The ratio of vapor pressure to the saturation pressure of water at a given temperature can be used to calculate:

○ A.   relative humidity
○ B.   specific humidity
○ C.   dew-point temperature
○ D.   wet-bulb temperature

77. Hot air at 200°C flows across a 50°C surface. If the heat transfer coefficient is 72 W/(m²·°C), the heat transfer rate (W) over 2 m² of the surface is most nearly:

- A. 300
- B. 5,625
- C. 11,250
- D. 21,600

78. Steam flows through a long pipe at a bulk temperature of 600 K and with a velocity of 6 m/s. If the pipe wall temperature is slightly less than 600 K, the steam film convection coefficient h_i[W/(m²·K)] is most nearly:

STEAM PROPERTIES:
$\rho = 10.844$ kg/m³
$\mu = 2.0417 \times 10^{-5}$ kg/(m·s)
$k_f = 0.0245$ W/(m·K)
$c_p = 1.344$ kJ/(kg·K)
Pr = 1.12

$r_i = 50$ mm

- A. 348
- B. 174
- C. 1.10
- D. 0.90

79. An infinitely long, 3-cm water pipe is laid on the ground surface A_3 as shown below. In order to calculate the radiative heat transfer between pairs of surfaces, you must know the shape factor (or view factor) F_{ij} between these surfaces. Assume infinitely large sky and ground surfaces. If the shape factor F_{13} between A_1 and A_3 is 1/2, the shape factor F_{12} between A_1 and A_2 is most nearly:

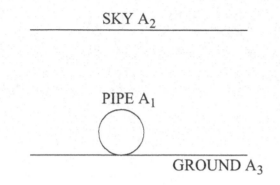

SKY A_2

PIPE A_1

GROUND A_3

- A.   1/4
- B.   1/2
- C.   3/4
- D.   1

80. An enclosure has Surfaces 1 and 2, each with an area of 4.0 m^2. The shape factor F_{1-2} is 0.275. Surfaces 1 and 2 are black surfaces with temperatures of 500°C and 400°C, respectively. The net rate of heat transfer (kW) by radiation between Surfaces 1 and 2 is most nearly:

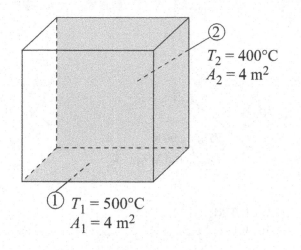

$T_2 = 400°C$
$A_2 = 4\ m^2$

$T_1 = 500°C$
$A_1 = 4\ m^2$

- ○ A.   2.30
- ○ B.   9.47
- ○ C.   22.3
- ○ D.   34.4

81.   The heat flux (W/m^2) through 1 m^2 of the steel/aluminum plate system shown is most nearly:

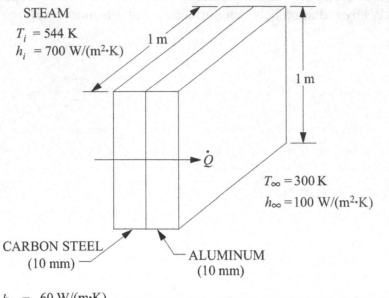

STEAM
T_i = 544 K
h_i = 700 W/(m^2·K)

1 m

1 m

$\dot{Q}$

T_∞ = 300 K
h_∞ = 100 W/(m^2·K)

CARBON STEEL
(10 mm)

ALUMINUM
(10 mm)

k_S = 60 W/(m·K)   (IGNORE RADIATION LOSSES AND CONTACT RESISTANCE
k_A = 240 W/(m·K)   BETWEEN THE CARBON STEEL AND ALUMINUM PLATES.)

- A.   17,800
- B.   19,800
- C.   21,000
- D.   153,000

82. For the steel/aluminum plate system shown, the interior temperature (K) between the steel and aluminum plate ($T_{S,A}$) is most nearly:

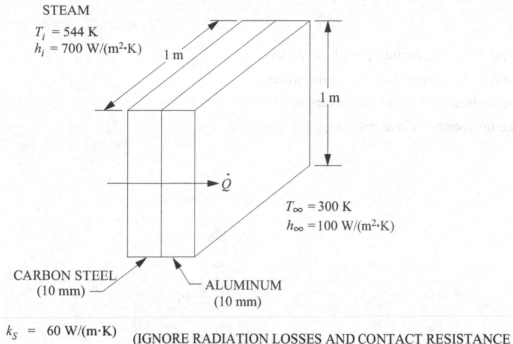

STEAM

T_i = 544 K
h_i = 700 W/(m²·K)

1 m

1 m

$\dot{Q}$

T_∞ = 300 K
h_∞ = 100 W/(m²·K)

CARBON STEEL
(10 mm)

ALUMINUM
(10 mm)

k_S = 60 W/(m·K)
k_A = 240 W/(m·K)

(IGNORE RADIATION LOSSES AND CONTACT RESISTANCE
BETWEEN THE CARBON STEEL AND ALUMINUM PLATES.)

- A. 544
- B. 514
- C. 510
- D. 500

83.   A heat exchanger is designed to heat liquid water from 150°C to 190°C inside tubes using steam condensing at 230°C on the outer surface of the tubes. For a constant flow rate, the effect of fouling of the heat transfer surfaces is to:

   O   A.   increase the temperature rise of the water
   O   B.   decrease the temperature rise of the water
   O   C.   increase heat exchanger effectiveness
   O   D.   make no change in heat exchanger effectiveness

Copyright © 2017 by NCEES   NEXT→

84. Water at 29°C flows through the inner pipe of a counterflow double-pipe heat exchanger, as shown in the figure. Hot oil at 204°C enters the annular space between the inner and outer pipes at a flow rate of 2.25 kg/s. The following physical data are known:

Property	Water	Oil
Specific heat, kJ/(kg·K)	4.186	3.5
Viscosity, kg/(m·s)	5.06×10^{-4}	6.3×10^{-3}
Density, kg/m^3	986.7	815.3

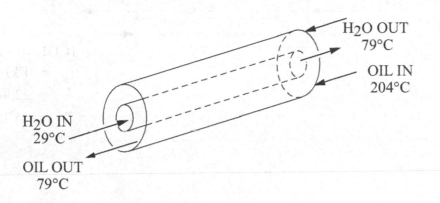

The mass flow rate of the water (kg/s) is most nearly:

- A. 2.25
- B. 4.70
- C. 6.58
- D. 19.7

85. Heat is transferred from a stream of hot water to a stream of cold air in the heat-exchanger arrangement shown in the figure below. The heat exchanger is assumed to be insulated from its surroundings, and the specific heats of the two streams are assumed to be constant. If the exit temperature of the hot stream is 65°C and the exit temperature of the cold stream is 60°C, the logarithmic-mean temperature difference for the heat exchanger is most nearly:

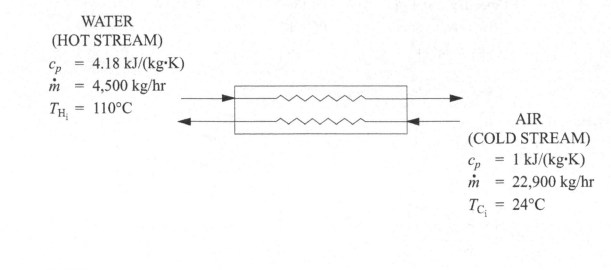

WATER
(HOT STREAM)

c_p = 4.18 kJ/(kg·K)

$\dot{m}$ = 4,500 kg/hr

T_{H_i} = 110°C

AIR
(COLD STREAM)

c_p = 1 kJ/(kg·K)

$\dot{m}$ = 22,900 kg/hr

T_{C_i} = 24°C

- A. 28.5°C
- B. 41.0°C
- C. 45.4°C
- D. 50.0°C

86. A heat exchanger is designed to heat liquid water from 150°C to 190°C inside tubes using steam condensing at 230°C on the outer surface of the tubes. The following data apply:

Tube material, copper	$k = 380$ W/(m·K)
Tube I.D.	2.5 cm
Tube O.D.	3.8 cm
h_i	6,000 W/(m^2·K)
h_o	12,000 W/(m^2·K)
Outside fouling resistance	9×10^{-5} m^2·K/W
Inside fouling resistance	7×10^{-4} m^2·K/W

The overall coefficient of heat transfer [W/(m^2·K)] based upon inside surface area is most nearly:

- O A. 1,000
- O B. 1,100
- O C. 4,250
- O D. 4,500

87. A resistance temperature detector (RTD) provides a resistance output that is related to temperature by:

$$R = R_o\,[1 + \alpha(T - T_o)],$$

where:

R = Resistance, Ω
R_o = Reference resistance, Ω
α = Coefficient, $°C^{-1}$
T = Temperature, $°C$
T_o = Reference temperature, $°C$

Consider an RTD with $R_o = 100\ \Omega$, $\alpha = 0.004°C^{-1}$, and $T_o = 0°C$.

The change in resistance (Ω) of the RTD for a 10°C change in temperature is most nearly:

- A. 0.04
- B. 0.4
- C. 4.0
- D. 100.4

88.   An automatic controls block diagram is shown below:

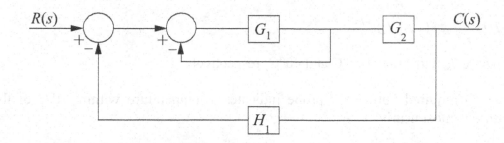

The single element relating the input to the output is best represented by:

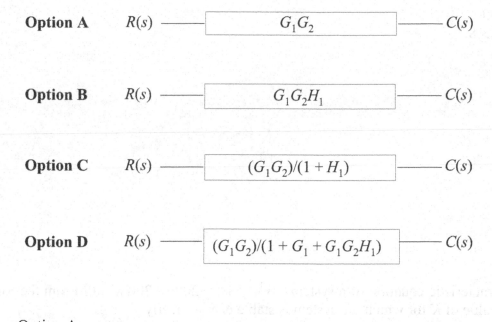

Option A $R(s)$ ———| $G_1 G_2$ |——— $C(s)$

Option B $R(s)$ ———| $G_1 G_2 H_1$ |——— $C(s)$

Option C $R(s)$ ———| $(G_1 G_2)/(1 + H_1)$ |——— $C(s)$

Option D $R(s)$ ———| $(G_1 G_2)/(1 + G_1 + G_1 G_2 H_1)$ |——— $C(s)$

- ○ A.   Option A
- ○ B.   Option B
- ○ C.   Option C
- ○ D.   Option D

89. A temperature probe has a time constant $\tau = 3.0$ s. The temperature indicated by the probe is given by the equation:

$$T(t) = T_o - (T_o - T_i)e^{-t/\tau}$$

where T_o and T_i are 140°C and 40°C, respectively.

The time (s) required before the probe indicates a temperature within ±1°C of the actual oil temperature is most nearly:

- A. 3.0
- B. 4.6
- C. 9.0
- D. 13.8

90. The characteristic equation of a system is $s^3 + 54s^2 + 200s + 200\,K = 0$. From the Routh test, the largest value of K for which the system is stable is most nearly:

- A. 5.2
- B. 8.3
- C. 12
- D. 54

91.   The transfer function relating a step input to the output of a control system is:

$$\frac{16}{s^3 + 0.8s^2 + 16s}$$

The natural frequency ω_n of the system and the damping ratio ς are most nearly:

- ○ A. $\omega_n = 2$ rad/s; $\varsigma = 0.1$
- ○ B. $\omega_n = 2$ rad/s; $\varsigma = 0.2$
- ○ C. $\omega_n = 4$ rad/s; $\varsigma = 0.1$
- ○ D. $\omega_n = 4$ rad/s; $\varsigma = 0.2$

92. A resistance temperature detector (RTD) provides a resistance output, R, that is related to temperature by:

$$R = R_0[1 + \alpha(T - T_0)]$$

where:

R = resistance, Ω
R_0 = reference resistance, 100 Ω
α = linear coefficient of resistance, $0.3925 \times 10^{-3}/°C$
T = temperature, °C
T_0 = reference temperature, 0°C

The uncertainty, U_R, may be calculated from the simplified Klein-McClintock equation:

$$U_R^2 = \left(\frac{\partial R}{\partial T} \, U_T \right)^2$$

where U_R and U_T are the uncertainties in variables R and T, respectively.

The resistance of the RTD, R, is 110 Ω, and this measured value has an uncertainty $U_R = \pm 0.1 \, \Omega$. The uncertainty in T is most nearly:

- A. ±0.0026°C
- B. ±0.0040°C
- C. ±0.1°C
- D. ±2.5°C

93. The beam is loaded as shown by a hanging 1,200-N force. The tensile stress (MPa) due to bending is most nearly:

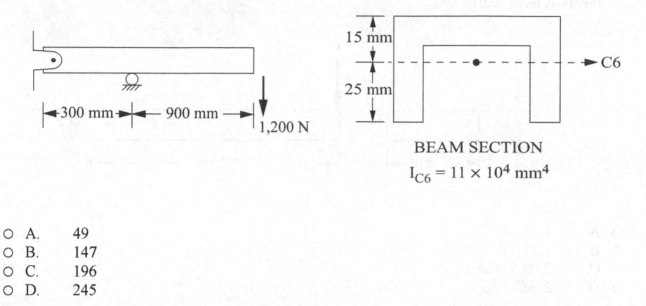

BEAM SECTION

$I_{C6} = 11 \times 10^4 \ mm^4$

- ○ A. 49
- ○ B. 147
- ○ C. 196
- ○ D. 245

Copyright © 2017 by NCEES

NEXT→

94. The load **P** varies between 0 and 40 N. The fatigue strength is $S_e = 200$ MPa, and the ultimate strength is $S_{ut} = 300$ MPa. The factor of safety determined by using the modified Goodman theory is most nearly:

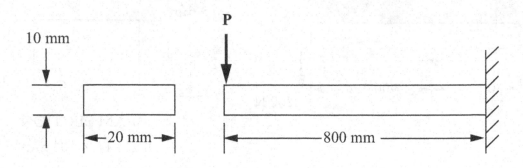

- ○ A.   1.00
- ○ B.   1.25
- ○ C.   2.00
- ○ D.   2.50

95. A helical compression spring has a wire diameter of 2.34 mm and an outside diameter of 15 mm. For a spring load of 150 N, the shear stress (MPa) in the spring is most nearly:

- ○ A.   342
- ○ B.   377
- ○ C.   412
- ○ D.   577

96. A helical compression spring has a spring constant of 38.525 N/mm and a free length of 190 mm. The force (N) required to compress the spring to a length of 125 mm is most nearly:

    ○ A.   1,500
    ○ B.   2,500
    ○ C.   4,800
    ○ D.   6,500

97. The pressure gage in an air cylinder reads 1,680 kPa. The cylinder is constructed of a 12-mm rolled-steel plate with an internal diameter of 700 mm. The tangential stress (MPa) inside the tank is most nearly:

    ○ A.   25
    ○ B.   50
    ○ C.   77
    ○ D.   100

98. The figure below shows an unpressurized vessel. Material properties are given with the figure.

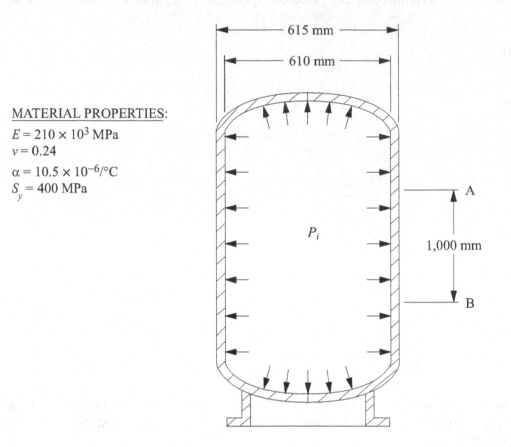

MATERIAL PROPERTIES:

$E = 210 \times 10^3$ MPa
$v = 0.24$
$\alpha = 10.5 \times 10^{-6}/°C$
$S_y = 400$ MPa

615 mm

610 mm

P_i

A

1,000 mm

B

VERTICAL-AXIS PRESSURE VESSEL SECTION

Assume the internal pressure is increased to P_i such that the stresses in the wall between Locations A and B are:

$\sigma_t = 46.2$ MPa
$\sigma_l = 23.1$ MPa
$\sigma_r = 0$

The increase in length (mm), along the outer wall, of the distance between Locations A and B due to the increase in pressure is most nearly:

- ○ A. 0.06
- ○ B. 0.11
- ○ C. 0.19
- ○ D. 0.22

99. The figure below shows a pressure vessel with an internal pressure P_i. Material properties are given with the figure.

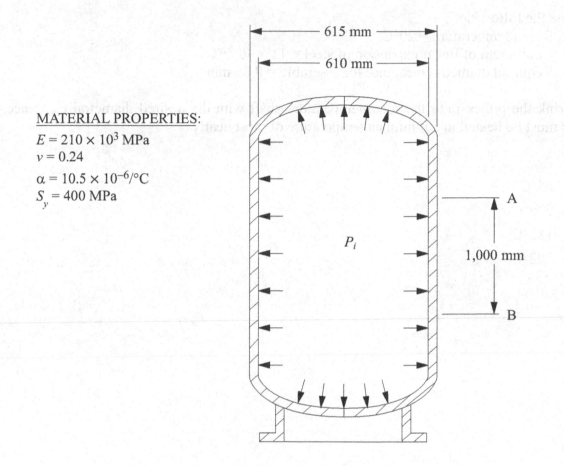

MATERIAL PROPERTIES:

$E = 210 \times 10^3$ MPa
$v = 0.24$
$\alpha = 10.5 \times 10^{-6}/°C$
$S_y = 400$ MPa

VERTICAL-AXIS PRESSURE VESSEL SECTION

If the internal pressure in the cylindrical pressure vessel shown is 600 kPa, the hoop or tangential stress (MPa) in the vessel wall between Cross Sections A and B is most nearly:

- ○ A. 18.4
- ○ B. 36.8
- ○ C. 73.5
- ○ D. 147

100. A steel pulley with a minimum room-temperature bore diameter of 100.00 mm is to be shrunk onto a steel shaft with a maximum room-temperature diameter of 100.15 mm.

Assume the following:
Room temperature = 20°C
Coefficient of linear expansion of steel = 11×10^{-6}/°C
Required diametral clearance for assembly = 0.05 mm

To shrink the pulley onto the room-temperature shaft with the desired diametral clearance, the pulley must be heated to a minimum temperature of most nearly:

- ○ A.   65°C
- ○ B.   136°C
- ○ C.   182°C
- ○ D.   202°C

SOLUTIONS

FE MECHANICAL SOLUTIONS

Detailed solutions for each question begin on the next page.

1	A	26	D	51	D	76	A
2	C	27	see solution	52	B	77	D
3	A	28	B	53	B	78	B
4	C	29	A	54	B	79	B
5	B	30	D	55	A	80	B
6	D	31	A	56	C	81	C
7	A	32	C	57	D	82	C
8	B	33	C	58	C	83	B
9	see solution	34	C	59	A	84	B
10	C	35	B	60	B	85	C
11	B	36	B	61	D	86	A
12	D	37	B	62	C	87	C
13	D	38	D	63	B	88	D
14	C	39	D	64	C	89	D
15	A	40	C	65	B	90	D
16	B	41	A	66	A	91	C
17	224/225	42	A	67	B	92	D
18	see solution	43	C	68	B	93	B
19	B	44	B	69	D	94	D
20	C	45	C	70	B, E	95	C
21	B	46	D	71	D	96	B
22	D	47	C	72	B	97	B
23	C	48	A	73	B	98	A
24	D	49	A	74	B	99	C
25	A	50	C	75	B	100	D

FE MECHANICAL SOLUTIONS

1. Refer to the Mathematics section of the *FE Reference Handbook*.

$(x - h)^2 + (y - k)^2 + (z - m)^2 = r^2$ with center at (h, k, m)

$(x - 0)^2 + (y - 1)^2 + (z - (-2))^2 = r^2$

$x^2 + (y - 1)^2 + (z + 2)^2 = 81$

THE CORRECT ANSWER IS: A

2. Refer to the Mathematics section of the *FE Reference Handbook*.

$$A = \int_2^5 3x^2 dx = x^3 \Big|_2^5 = 5^3 - 2^3$$

$$= 117$$

THE CORRECT ANSWER IS: C

3. Define a differential strip with length $(x - 0)$ and height dy.

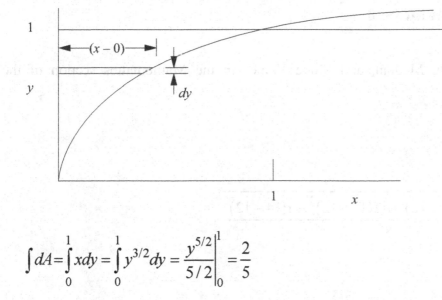

$$\int dA = \int_0^1 x\,dy = \int_0^1 y^{3/2} dy = \frac{y^{5/2}}{5/2}\Big|_0^1 = \frac{2}{5}$$

THE CORRECT ANSWER IS: A

FE MECHANICAL SOLUTIONS

4. The cross product of vectors **A** and **B** is a vector perpendicular to **A** and **B**.

$$\begin{vmatrix} \mathbf{i} & \mathbf{j} & \mathbf{k} \\ 2 & 4 & 0 \\ 1 & 1 & -1 \end{vmatrix} = \mathbf{i}(-4) - \mathbf{j}(-2-0) + \mathbf{k}(2-4) = -4\mathbf{i} + 2\mathbf{j} - 2\mathbf{k}$$

To obtain a unit vector, divide by the magnitude.

$$\text{Magnitude} = \sqrt{(-4)^2 + 2^2 + (-2)^2} = \sqrt{24} = 2\sqrt{6}$$

$$\frac{-4\mathbf{i} + 2\mathbf{j} - 2\mathbf{k}}{2\sqrt{6}} = \frac{-2\mathbf{i} + \mathbf{j} - \mathbf{k}}{\sqrt{6}}$$

THE CORRECT ANSWER IS: C

5. Refer to the Mathematics section of the *FE Reference Handbook.*

$$\text{Area} = \frac{0.5}{2}\left[0^2 + 2(0.5)^2 + 2(1.0)^2 + 2(1.5)^2 + (2)^2\right] = 2.75$$

THE CORRECT ANSWER IS: B

6. From Dispersion, Mean, Median, and Mode Values in the Mathematics section of the *FE Reference Handbook*:

$$\sigma = \sqrt{\frac{1}{N}\Sigma(x_1 - \mu)^2}$$

$$\sigma = \sqrt{\frac{4(11-12)^2 + 1(12-12)^2 + 2(13-12)^2 + 1(14-12)^2}{8}}$$

$$\sigma = 1.118$$

THE CORRECT ANSWER IS: D

FE MECHANICAL SOLUTIONS

7. $8 - 15.5 = 7.5$

$\dfrac{7.5}{2.5} = 3$ standard deviations

From the Unit Normal Distribution table in the Engineering Probability and Statistics section of the *FE Reference Handbook*.

For $x = 3$, $R(x) = 0.0013$

THE CORRECT ANSWER IS: A

8. Accuracy increases with increasing sample size.

THE CORRECT ANSWER IS: B

9.

x	$x - \bar{x}$	$(x - \bar{x})^2$
4	−1	1
4	−1	1
7	2	4
$\Sigma = 15$		$\Sigma = 6$

$\bar{x} = 15/3 = 5 = $ mean

Median is the value of $\left(\dfrac{n+1}{2}\right)^{\text{th}}$ item. $\left(\dfrac{3+1}{2}\right) = 2$ items

Median $= 4$

$\sigma^2 = (1/N) \displaystyle\sum_{i=1}^{N}(X_1 - \mu)^2 = (1/3)(6) = 2 = $ variance

Statistical Quantities

Mean   5

Variance 2

Median   4

THE CORRECT ANSWERS ARE SHOWN ABOVE.

10.   The following formulas are in the first five rows of Column B:

    1. $A1^3 + A$1^2 - 3
    2. $A2^3 + A$1^2 - 3
    3. $A3^3 + A$1^2 - 3
    4. $A4^3 + A$1^2 - 3
    5. $A5^3 + A$1^2 - 3

    In spreadsheet equation format, the formula in Cell B5 is:

    $A5^3 + A$1^2 - 3

    THE CORRECT ANSWER IS: C

11.

Row	Column A	Value of A
4	6	6
5	A4 + A4	12
6	A5 + A4	18
7	A6 + A4	24

    THE CORRECT ANSWER IS: B

12.

Step	VAR
1	0
2	2
3	4
4	6

    EXIT LOOP

    At the conclusion of the routine, VAR = 6.

    THE CORRECT ANSWER IS: D

13.

First Round	Second Round
$Q = 1 + 2 = 3$	$Q = 3 + 2 = 5$
$K = 2 \times 3 = 6$	$K = 6 \times 5 = 30$
$3 > 3$ NO!	$5 > 3$ YES!
	$\therefore Q = 5$

THE CORRECT ANSWER IS: D

14. Refer to the Ethics section of the *FE Reference Handbook*. Section B in the Rules of Professional Conduct states:

> Licensees shall undertake assignments only when qualified by education or experience in the specific technical fields of engineering or surveying involved.

THE CORRECT ANSWER IS: C

15. Refer to the NCEES Rules of Professional Conduct in the Ethics section of the *FE Reference Handbook*.

THE CORRECT ANSWER IS: A

16. The characteristic equation for a first-order, linear, homogeneous differential equation is:

$$r + 5 = 0$$

which has a root at $r = -5$.

Refer to Differential Equations in the Mathematics section of the *FE Reference Handbook*. The form of the solution is then:

$$y = Ce^{-\alpha t} \text{ where } \alpha = a \text{ and } \quad a = 5 \text{ for this problem}$$

C is determined from the boundary condition.

$$1 = Ce^{-5(0)}$$
$$C = 1$$

Then, $y = e^{-5t}$

THE CORRECT ANSWER IS: B

17. Annual cost: $= \$900(A/P, 8\%, 5) + \$50 - \$300(A/F, 8\%, 5)$
$= \$900(0.2505) + \$50 - \$300(0.1705)$
$= \$225.45 + \$50 - \$51.15$
$= \$224.30$

THE CORRECT ANSWER IS: 224 OR 225

FE MECHANICAL SOLUTIONS

18. Compute P (present value) given A (the periodic value) P/A. Uniform series present worth factors are described in the Engineering Economics section of the *FE Reference Handbook*.

Factor Table –i = 2.00%

n	P/F	P/A	P/G	F/P	F/A	A/P	A/F	A/G
1	0.9804	0.9804	0.0000	1.0200	1.0000	1.0200	1.0000	0.0000
2	0.9612	1.9416	0.9612	1.0404	2.0200	0.5150	0.4950	0.4950
3	0.9423	2.8839	2.8458	1.0612	3.0604	0.3468	0.3268	0.9868
4	0.9238	3.8077	5.6173	1.0824	4.1216	0.2626	0.2426	1.4752
5	0.9057	4.7135	9.2403	1.1041	5.2040	0.2122	0.1922	1.9604
6	0.8880	5.6014	13.6801	1.1262	6.3081	0.1785	0.1585	2.4423
7	0.8706	6.4720	18.9035	1.1487	7.4343	0.1545	0.1345	2.9208
8	0.8535	7.3255	24.8779	1.1717	8.5830	0.1365	0.1165	3.3961
9	0.8368	8.1622	31.5720	1.1951	9.7546	0.1225	0.1025	3.8681
10	0.8203	8.9826	38.9551	1.2190	10.9497	0.1113	0.0913	4.3367
11	0.8043	9.7868	46.9977	1.2434	12.1687	0.1022	0.0822	4.8021
12	0.7885	10.5753	55.6712	1.2682	13.4121	0.0946	0.0746	5.2642
13	0.7730	11.3484	64.9475	1.2936	14.6803	0.0881	0.0681	5.7231
14	0.7579	12.1062	74.7999	1.3195	15.9739	0.0826	0.0626	6.1786
15	0.7430	12.8493	85.2021	1.3459	17.2934	0.0778	0.0578	6.6309
16	0.7284	13.5777	96.1288	1.3728	18.6393	0.0737	0.0537	7.0799
17	0.7142	14.2919	107.5554	1.4002	20.0121	0.0700	0.0500	7.5256
18	0.7002	14.9920	119.4581	1.4282	21.4123	0.0677	0.0467	7.9681
19	0.6864	15.6785	131.8139	1.4568	22.8406	0.0638	0.0438	8.4073
20	0.6730	16.3514	144.6003	1.4859	24.2974	0.0612	0.0412	8.8433
21	0.6598	17.0112	157.7959	1.5157	25.7833	0.0588	0.0388	9.2760
22	0.6468	17.6580	171.3795	1.5460	27.2990	0.0566	0.0366	9.7055
23	0.6342	18.2922	185.3309	1.5769	28.8450	0.0547	0.0347	10.1317
24	0.6217	18.9139	199.6305	1.6084	30.4219	0.0529	0.0329	10.5547
25	0.6095	19.5235	214.2592	1.6406	32.0303	0.0512	0.0312	10.9745
30	0.5521	22.3965	291.7164	1.8114	40.5681	0.0446	0.0246	13.0251
40	0.4529	27.3555	461.9931	2.2080	60.4020	0.0366	0.0166	16.8885
50	0.3715	31.4236	642.3606	2.6916	84.5794	0.0318	0.0118	20.4420
60	0.3048	34.7609	823.6975	3.2810	114.0515	0.0288	0.0088	23.6961
100	0.1380	43.0984	1,464.7527	7.2446	312.2323	0.0232	0.0032	33.9863

THE CORRECT ANSWER IS SHADED ABOVE.

19. The power dissipated in a resistor can be found by applying the equation $P = \dfrac{V^2}{R}$.

The voltage across the 90-Ω resistor is $100 - 60 = 40$ V. Therefore, $P = \dfrac{40^2}{90\ \Omega} = 17.78$ W

THE CORRECT ANSWER IS: B

20. Refer to the Electrical and Computer section of the *FE Reference Handbook.*

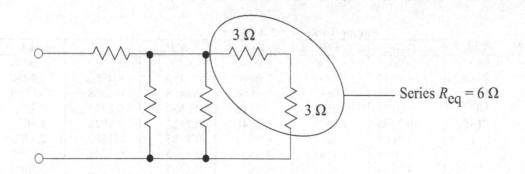

Series $R_{eq} = 6\ \Omega$

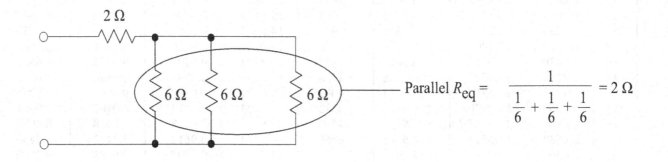

Parallel $R_{eq} = \dfrac{1}{\dfrac{1}{6} + \dfrac{1}{6} + \dfrac{1}{6}} = 2\ \Omega$

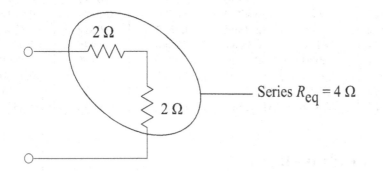

Series $R_{eq} = 4\ \Omega$

THE CORRECT ANSWER IS: C

21. Refer to the Electrical and Computer section of the *FE Reference Handbook*.

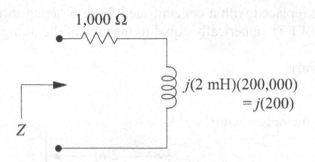

The impedance of the resistor is $Z_R = R = 1,000\ \Omega$.
The impedance of the inductor is $Z_L = j\omega L = j(100,000)(0.002) = j200\ \Omega$
Since they are in series, $Z = 1,000 + j200\ \Omega$

THE CORRECT ANSWER IS: B

22. Refer to Complex Power in the Electrical and Computer Engineering section of the *FE Reference Handbook* for the equation:

$$P = V_{rms}\, I_{rms}\, \cos\theta$$

$$pf = \cos\theta = \frac{P}{V_{rms}\, I_{rms}}$$

$$= \frac{1,500}{(115)(15)}$$

$$= 0.87$$

THE CORRECT ANSWER IS: D

23. Refer to Systems of Forces in the Statics section of the *FE Reference Handbook.*

The triangular force distribution can be replaced with a concentrated force **F** acting through the centroid of the triangle. The magnitude of **F** is numerically equal to the area of the triangle.

$\mathbf{F} = 1/2 \text{ (base)(height)} = 1/2 \text{ (3 m)(8 kN/m)}$
$\mathbf{F} = 12 \text{ kN}$

Sum the moments about Point A so that the only unknown is R_B.

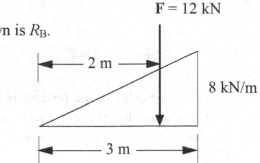

$\Sigma M_A = 0$
$6R_B - 5\mathbf{F} = 0$
$6R_B - 5(12 \text{ kN}) = 0$
$R_B = 10 \text{ kN}$

THE CORRECT ANSWER IS: C

24.

$$R_y = \Sigma F_y = \frac{12}{13}(260) + \frac{3}{5}(300) - 50 = 370$$

$$R_x = \Sigma F_x = -\frac{5}{13}(260) + \frac{4}{5}(300) = 140$$

$$R = \sqrt{R_x^2 + R_y^2} = \sqrt{370^2 + 140^2}$$

$$R = 396 \text{ N}$$

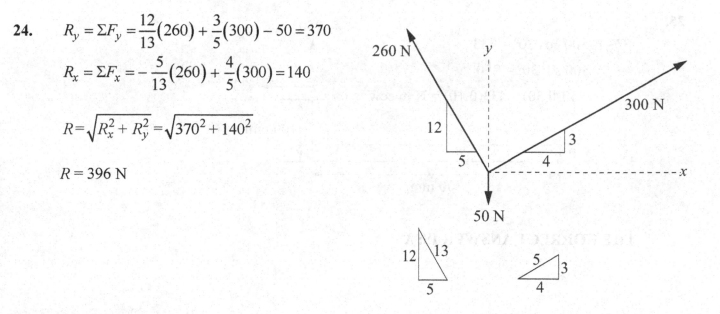

THE CORRECT ANSWER IS: D

25.

$F_H = 500 \cos 30^\circ = 433$

$F_V = 500 \sin 30^\circ = 250$

$M_P = 250(0.30) - 433(0.10) = \text{N·m ccw}$

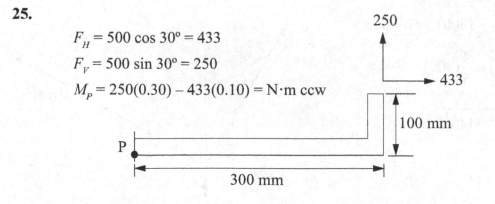

THE CORRECT ANSWER IS: A

26. Refer to Plane Truss: Method of Sections in the Statics section of the *FE Reference Handbook*.

Place a hypothetical cut as shown below, exposing Member BC as an external force. Then sum the moments about the point so the F_{BC} provides the only unknown moment.

$$\sum M_I = 0$$

$$\sum M_I = (5 F_{BC}) - (5 \times 3) - (10 \times 3) - (15 \times 3) = 0$$

$$0 = 5 F_{BC} - 15 - 30 - 45$$

$$F_{BC} = 3 + 6 + 9$$

$$F_{BC} = 18 \text{ kN}$$

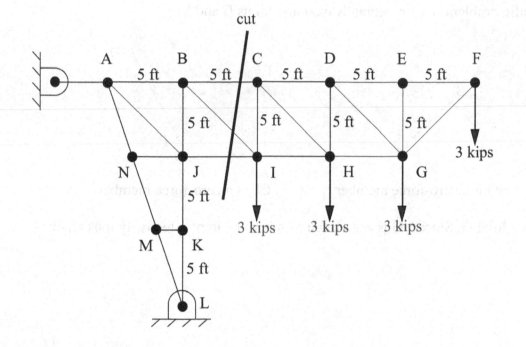

THE CORRECT ANSWER IS: D

27. Zero-force members usually occur at joints where members are aligned as follows:

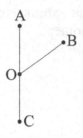

That is, joints where two members are along the same line (OA and OC) and the third member is at some arbitrary angle create zero-force members. That member (OB) is a zero-force member because the forces in OA and OC must be equal and opposite.

For this specific problem, we immediately examine Joints B and E:

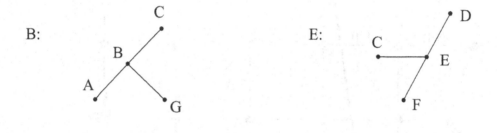

B:

E:

BG is a zero-force member   CE is a zero-force member

Now, examine Joint G. Since BG is zero-force member, the joint effectively looks like:

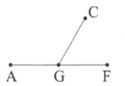

and, therefore, CG is another zero-force member.

Finally, examine Joint C. Since both CG and CE are zero-force members, the joint effectively looks like:

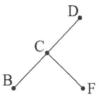

and, therefore, CF is another zero-force member. Thus, BG, CE, CG, and CF are the zero-force members.

FE MECHANICAL SOLUTIONS

27. **(Continued)**

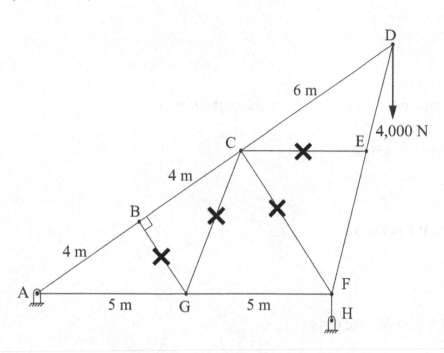

THE CORRECT ANSWERS ARE MARKED ABOVE.

28. The location of the centroid from the *y*-axis in the direction parallel to the *x*-axis is given by:

$$\bar{x} = \frac{1}{A} \int_A x \, dA \qquad \text{where } dA = (y_2 - y_1) \, dx$$

$$\bar{x} = \frac{\int_0^3 x \left(x - \frac{x^2}{3} \right) dx}{\int_0^3 \left(x - \frac{x^2}{3} \right) dx} \qquad \text{or} \qquad \bar{x} = \frac{\int_0^3 \left(x^2 - \frac{1}{3} x^3 \right) dx}{\int_0^3 \left(x - \frac{1}{3} x^2 \right) dx}$$

THE CORRECT ANSWER IS: B

29. Refer to the Belt Friction section in the Statics chapter of the *FE Reference Handbook*.

$$F_1 = F_2\, e^{\mu\theta}$$

$$3{,}000 = 450e^{\mu\pi}$$

Set μ equal to μ_s, the static coefficient; and $\theta = \pi$, the angle of wrap.

$$\therefore \mu_s \pi = \ln \frac{3{,}000}{450}, \ \mu = \frac{1}{\pi} \ln\!\left(\frac{3{,}000}{450}\right)$$

$$\mu_s = 0.60$$

THE CORRECT ANSWER IS: A

30. Normal to the plane:

$$\Sigma F_n = 0: \ N - mg \cos \phi = 0 \rightarrow N = mg \cos \phi$$

Tangent to the plane:

$$\Sigma F_t = 0: \ -mg \sin \phi + \mu N = 0$$

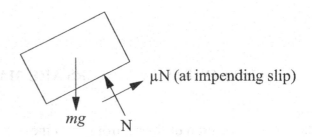

$$\therefore -mg \sin \phi + \mu mg \cos \phi = 0$$

$$\frac{\sin \phi}{\cos \phi} = \tan \phi = \mu$$

$$\tan \phi = 0.25$$

THE CORRECT ANSWER IS: D

FE MECHANICAL SOLUTIONS

31. Refer to the Friction section in the Dynamics chapter of the *FE Reference Handbook*.

The upper frictional force due to Block A on Block B is
$$F_U = 0.2\, m_A g$$
$$= 0.2(2)(9.81) = 3.924 \text{ N}$$

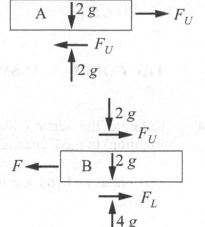

The lower frictional force on Block B at the bottom surface is
$$F_L = 0.4(m_A + m_B)g$$
$$= 0.4(2+2)9.81 = 15.696 \text{ N}$$

Then from the Kinetics section,

$$\sum F = ma$$
$$F - F_L - F_U = ma$$
$$30 - 15.696 - 3.924 = 2a$$
$$a = 5.19 \approx 5.2 \text{ m/s}^2$$

THE CORRECT ANSWER IS: A

32. Refer to the Work and Energy section in the Dynamics chapter of the *FE Reference Handbook*.

$$T_2 + U_2 = T_1 + U_1 + W_{1\to2}, \qquad W_{1\to2} = -Fx$$

$$\frac{1}{2}mv_2^2 = \frac{1}{2}mv_1^2 - \mu_k mgx$$

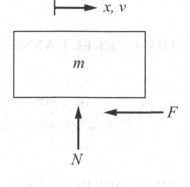

Cancel m to obtain $\to \frac{1}{2}(10)^2 = \frac{1}{2}v_1^2 - 0.2(9.81)(20)$

$$v_1 = 13.4 \text{ m/s}$$

$$F = \mu_k mg$$

THE CORRECT ANSWER IS: C

33. $T_1 + U_1 + W_{1 \to 2} = T_2 + U_2$

$0 + 0 + Fs = 1/2 \, mv^2 + mgh$

$5F = 1/2 \, (2)(8)^2 + (2)(9.81)(3)$

$F = 24.6 \text{ N}$

THE CORRECT ANSWER IS: C

34. Refer to the section Plane Motion of a Rigid Body—Kinematics (Instantaneous Center of Rotation) in the Dynamics chapter of the *FE Reference Handbook.*

The crank and rod are two rigid bodies. At the moment when $\theta = 90°$, v_P is desired (piston speed).

$v_C = 50 \text{ mm} \times 377 \text{ rad/s} = 18,850 \text{ mm/s}$

Both points are on the rod. By the method of instantaneous centers, the center of rotation is located where the line at P, $\perp$ to v_P, intersects the line at C, $\perp$ to v_C.

v_C is parallel to v_P so these meet at infinity. Thus the rotation of rod PC is 0, or $\omega_{PC} = 0$.

Since there is no rotation at this instant, *all* points of the rod move with the same velocity and

$v_P = v_C = 18,850 \text{ mm/s}$ because $\overline{v}_P = \overline{v}_C + \overline{\omega}_{PC} \times \overline{r}_{P/C}$ and $\omega_{PC} = 0$.

THE CORRECT ANSWER IS: C

35. $\angle V_{PA} = \theta_3 + \delta_P + 90°$

$\qquad = 15° + 30° + 90° = 135°$

THE CORRECT ANSWER IS: B

36. The kinetic energy, T, when the object is at Q, is:

$T = 1/2 \, mv^2 = 1/2 \left(1.5 \text{ kg}\right)\left(2 \text{ m/s}\right)^2 = 3 \text{ J}$

THE CORRECT ANSWER IS: B

37. Refer to Principle of Work and Energy in the Dynamics section of the *FE Reference Handbook*.

$T_2 + U_2 = T_1 + U_1 + W_{1 \to 2}$

$W_{1 \to 2} = 0$

$T_1 = 0$

$T_2 = \dfrac{1}{2}mv_2^2$

$U_1 = mgh_1$

$U_2 = 0$

$\dfrac{1}{2}mv_2^2 = mg(2.5) \Rightarrow v_2 = \sqrt{5g} = \sqrt{5(9.81)} = 7\,\text{m/s}$

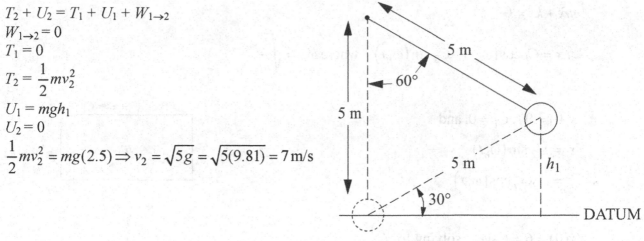

$h_1 = 5 \sin 30° = 2.5$

THE CORRECT ANSWER IS: B

38.   Refer to the Free Vibration section in the Dynamics chapter of the *FE Reference Handbook*.

$$m\ddot{x} + kx = 0$$

$$\therefore x = C_1 \cos\left(\omega_n t\right) + C_2 \sin\left(\omega_n t\right) \quad \text{where } \omega_n = \sqrt{\frac{k}{m}}$$

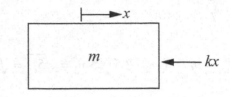

$x(0) = 0 \therefore C_1 = 0$, and

$$x = C_2 \sin\left(\omega_n t\right)$$

$$\dot{x} = C_2 \omega_n \cos\left(\omega_n t\right)$$

$\dot{x}(0) = 6 = C_2 \omega_n$, solving for C_2

$$C_2 = \frac{6}{\omega_n}$$

$$\ddot{x} = -C_2 \omega_n^2 \sin\left(\omega_n t\right)$$

$$\ddot{x} = -6\omega_n \sin\left(\omega_n t\right)$$

$$\ddot{x} = -6\sqrt{\frac{9}{4}} \sin\left(\omega_n t\right)$$

$$\ddot{x} = -9 \text{ m/s}^2 \sin\left(\omega_n t\right)$$

$$\therefore \ddot{x}_{max} = 9 \text{ m/s}^2$$

THE CORRECT ANSWER IS: D

39. $\dfrac{10 \text{ m}}{10 \text{ kN}} = \dfrac{x}{6 \text{ kN}}$

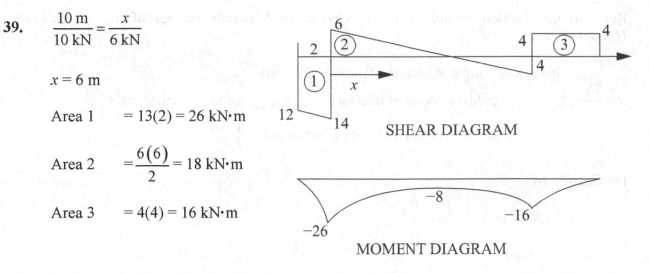

SHEAR DIAGRAM

$x = 6$ m

Area 1 $= 13(2) = 26$ kN·m

Area 2 $= \dfrac{6(6)}{2} = 18$ kN·m

Area 3 $= 4(4) = 16$ kN·m

MOMENT DIAGRAM

Maximum magnitude of the bending moment is 26 kN·m.

THE CORRECT ANSWER IS: D

---

40. From Uniaxial Loading and Deformation in the Mechanics of Materials section of the *FE Reference Handbook*, the uniaxial deformation is:

$$\text{Deformation} = \delta = \frac{\text{PL}}{\text{AE}} = \frac{(5,000)(0.25)}{\left(1,250 \times 10^{-6}\right)\left(200 \times 10^{9}\right)} = 5.0 \times 10^{-6} \text{ m} = 5.0 \text{ } \mu\text{m}$$

THE CORRECT ANSWER IS: C

---

41. $\Sigma F = PA = \left(1.4 \times 10^{6}\right)\left(\dfrac{\pi(0.5)^2}{4}\right) = F_{\text{rod}}$

$F_{\text{rod}} = 275 \text{ kN} = \sigma A = 68 \times 10^{6} A$

$A = 40.4 \times 10^{-4} \text{ m}^2$

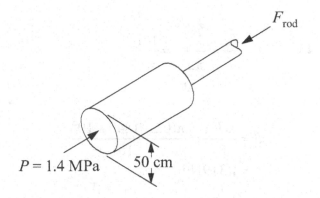

F_{rod}

$P = 1.4$ MPa   50 cm

THE CORRECT ANSWER IS: A

42. Refer to the Torsion section in the Mechanics of Materials chapter of the *FE Reference Handbook*.

$$\tau = \frac{Tr}{J}$$

where T = Torque at section of interest (N · mm)

r = radius to point of interest (mm), $r_{outside}$ for maximum shear

J = section (polar) moment of inertia $\left(mm^4\right)$

For Section BC

$$T = 1,000 \, \text{N} \cdot \text{m}$$

$$r = \frac{75}{2} \, \text{mm}$$

$$J = \frac{\pi\left(75^4 - 50^4\right)}{32} \, \text{mm}^4$$

Hence the maximum torsional shear stress is given by

$$\tau = \frac{\left(1,000,000 \, \text{N} \cdot \text{mm}\right)\left(\dfrac{75}{2} \, \text{mm}\right)}{\dfrac{\pi\left(75^4 - 50^4\right)}{32} \, \text{mm}^4}$$

$$= 15 \, \text{MPa}$$

THE CORRECT ANSWER IS: A

43. $$\tau = \frac{Tr}{J} = \frac{T\dfrac{d}{2}}{\dfrac{\pi d^4}{32}} = \frac{16T}{\pi d^3}$$

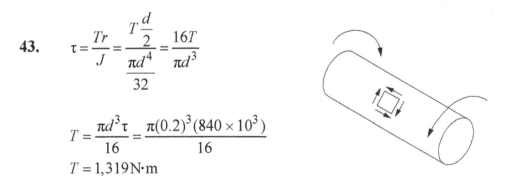

$$T = \frac{\pi d^3 \tau}{16} = \frac{\pi(0.2)^3\left(840 \times 10^3\right)}{16}$$

$$T = 1,319 \, \text{N} \cdot \text{m}$$

THE CORRECT ANSWER IS: C

44.   Refer to Mohr's Circle in the Mechanics of Material section of the *FE Reference Handbook*.

From a constructed Mohr's Circle, the maximum inplane shear stress is $\tau_{max} = R$.

$$R = \sqrt{\left(\frac{\sigma_x - \sigma_y}{2}\right)^2 + \tau_{xy}^2}$$

$$R = \sqrt{\left(\frac{40 - 20}{2}\right)^2 + 10^2}$$

$$R = \sqrt{200}$$

$$R = 14.1 \text{ ksi}$$

THE CORRECT ANSWER IS: B

45. The stress at Point O may be represented as

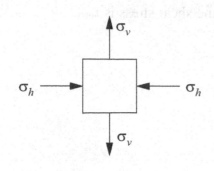

where $\sigma = \dfrac{\text{Load}}{\text{Area}}$

$$\sigma_h = \frac{10{,}000 \text{ N}}{(100 \text{ mm})(10 \text{ mm})} = -10 \text{ MPa}$$

$$\sigma_v = \frac{5{,}000 \text{ N}}{(100 \text{ mm})(10 \text{ mm})} = 5 \text{ MPa}$$

Since σ_h is compressive,

$$\sigma_1 = 5 \text{ MPa}, \ \sigma_2 = 0 \text{ MPa}, \ \sigma_3 = -10 \text{ MPa},$$

Thus

$$\tau_{max} = \frac{\sigma_1 - \sigma_3}{2}$$
$$= \frac{5 - (-10)}{2}$$
$$= 7.5 \text{ MPa}$$

THE CORRECT ANSWER IS: C

46. The Euler formula is used for elastic stability of relatively long columns, subjected to concentric axial loads in compression.

THE CORRECT ANSWER IS: D

47. Cold-working decreases the recrystallization temperature, ductility, and slipping or twining takes place. During cold work, grains become elongated instead of equiaxed.

   THE CORRECT ANSWER IS: C

48. The diffusion equation is found in the Materials Science/Structure of Matter section in the *FE Reference Handbook*.

   $$D = D_o e^{-Q/RT}$$

   Since D is the same for FCC iron and HCP titanium

   $$5.1 \times 10^{-4} \exp\left[-\frac{182,126}{8.314\,T}\right] = 0.2 \times 10^{-4} \exp\left[-\frac{142,350}{8.314\,T}\right]$$

   $$-\frac{21,906}{T} = \ln\left[\frac{0.2 \times 10^{-4}}{5.1 \times 10^{-4}}\right] - \frac{17,122}{T}$$

   $$\frac{4,784}{T} = 3.2387 \Rightarrow T = 1,477 \text{ K} = 1,204°C$$

   THE CORRECT ANSWER IS: A

49. This is the definition of hot working.

   THE CORRECT ANSWER IS: A

50. Refer to the Binary Phase diagrams in the Material Science/Structure of Matter chapter of the *FE Reference Handbook*.

   The eutectic composition is the point at which the liquid phase transforms directly to two solid phases. For the Ag-Cu phase diagram, the $L \rightarrow \alpha + \beta$ occurs only at 28.1% Cu and 71.9% Ag.

   THE CORRECT ANSWER IS: C

51.

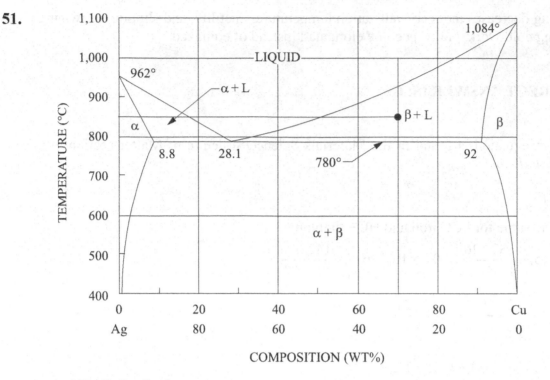

At 850°C, β + L phases are present.

THE CORRECT ANSWER IS: D

52. Refer to the hardenability curves for agitated oil in the Materials Science/Structure of Matter chapter in the *FE Reference Handbook*.

Find the intersection of 40-mm diameter with the center cooling rate curve C.. Read the distance from the quenched end as 12.5 mm.

Then, go to the Jominy hardenability curves graph for a 4140 steel and a 12.5-mm distance from the quenched end. The R_c hardness is 52. Therefore, 52 is the expected center hardness for a 4140 steel of diameter 40 mm when quenched in an agitated oil bath.

THE CORRECT ANSWER IS: B

53. Aluminum is anodic relative to copper and, therefore, will corrode to protect the copper.

THE CORRECT ANSWER IS: B

54. Refer to Stress Concentration in the Brittle Materials section of the Materials Science/Structure of Matter chapter in the *FE Reference Handbook*.

Critical crack length: $K_I = y\sigma\sqrt{\pi a}$

Solving for critical a_c yields $\quad a_c = \left(\dfrac{K_{Ic}}{yS_y}\right)^2 \dfrac{1}{\pi} = \left(\dfrac{44}{1.1 \times 345}\right)^2 \dfrac{1}{\pi}$

$$a_c = 4.3 \text{ mm}$$

THE CORRECT ANSWER IS: B

55. Refer to the Fluid Mechanics section of the *FE Reference Handbook*.

Units of absolute dynamic viscosity (μ) are kg/(m·s).

Units of kinematic viscosity (v) are m^2/s.

$\therefore$ The relationship between the two is:

$v = \mu/\rho$ where ρ is the density in kg/m^3.

$v = 1.5/1.263(1{,}000) = 0.001188 = 1.19 \times 10^{-3}$.

THE CORRECT ANSWER IS: A

56. Refer to the Fluid Mechanics section of the *FE Reference Handbook*.

$$\tau_t = \mu\left(\frac{dv}{dy}\right)$$

where τ_t = shear stress and

$\dfrac{dv}{dy}$ = rate of shear deformation

Hence, μ is the ratio of shear stress to the rate of shear deformation.

THE CORRECT ANSWER IS: C

FE MECHANICAL SOLUTIONS

57. Refer to the Fluid Mechanics section of the *FE Reference Handbook*.

THE CORRECT ANSWER IS: D

58. The mean pressure of the fluid acting on the gate is evaluated at the mean height, and the center of pressure is 2/3 of the height from the top; thus, the total force of the fluid is:

$$F_f = \rho g \frac{H}{2}(H) = 1,600(9.807)\frac{3}{2}(3) = 70,610 \text{ N}$$

and its point of application is 1.00 m above the hinge. A moment balance about the hinge gives:

$$F(3) - F_f(1) = 0$$

$$F = \frac{F_f}{3} = \frac{70,610}{3} = 23,537 \text{ N}$$

THE CORRECT ANSWER IS: C

59. Refer to the Fluid Mechanics section of the *FE Reference Handbook*.

$$v = \sqrt{2gh} = \sqrt{2 \times 9.81 \times 3} = 7.67 \text{ m/s}$$

THE CORRECT ANSWER IS: A

60. $Q = A_1 V_1 = (0.01 \text{ m}^2)(30 \text{ m/s})$
     $= 0.3 \text{ m}^3/\text{s}$

Since the water jet is deflected perpendicularly, the force **F** must deflect the total horizontal momentum of the water.

$\mathbf{F} = \rho Q V = (1,000 \text{ kg/m}^3)(0.3 \text{ m}^3/\text{s})(30 \text{ m/s}) = 9,000 \text{ N} = 9.0 \text{ kN}$

THE CORRECT ANSWER IS: B

61. Use the mass flow rate, density, and diameter to determine the flow velocity.

$\dot{m} = \rho A V$ Refer to the One-Dimensional Flows section in the Fluid Mechanics chapter of the *FE Reference Handbook*.

Solve for velocity

$$V = \frac{\dot{m}}{\rho A} \qquad A = \frac{\pi}{4} D^2$$

Substitute:

$$V = \frac{\dot{m}}{\rho \frac{\pi}{4} D^2} = \frac{4\dot{m}}{\pi \rho D^2}$$

Use the equation for Reynolds number written in terms of dynamic viscosity:

$$Re = \frac{VD\rho}{\mu}$$ Refer to the Similitude section in the Fluid Mechanics chapter of the *FE Reference Handbook*.

Substitute the velocity expression and simplify:

$$Re = \frac{4\dot{m}D\rho}{\pi \rho D^2 \mu} = \frac{4\dot{m}}{\pi D \mu}$$

Substitute the given values and solve:

$$Re = \frac{(4)(22.7 \text{ kg/s})}{(\pi)(0.1023 \text{ m})\left(2.32 \times 10^{-4} \text{ kg/(m·s)}\right)}$$

$$Re = 1,217,800 \cong 1,200,000$$

THE CORRECT ANSWER IS: D

FE MECHANICAL SOLUTIONS

62. The Reynolds number is found in the Fluid Mechanics section of the *FE Reference Handbook*.

$$\text{Re} = \frac{VD\rho}{\mu}$$

$$V = 1.5 \text{ m/s}$$

$$D = 2.5 \text{ cm} = 2.5 \times 10^{-2} \text{ m}$$

$$\upsilon = 1.59 \times 10^{-4} \frac{\text{N} \cdot \text{s}}{\text{m}^2}$$

$$\rho = 898 \text{ kg/m}^3$$

$$\text{Re} = \frac{\left(1.5 \text{ m/s}\right)\left(2.5 \times 10^{-2} \text{ m}\right)\left(898 \text{ kg/m}^3\right)}{1.59 \times 10^{-4} \text{ N} \cdot \text{s/m}^2}$$

$$= 211,792 \frac{(\text{m/s})(\text{m})(\text{kg})}{\left(\text{N} \cdot \text{s/m}^2\right)\left(\text{m}^3\right)} \qquad 1 \text{ N} = 1 \text{ kg} \cdot \text{m/s}^2$$

Verify units $\dfrac{(\text{m/s})(\text{m})(\text{kg})}{\left(\dfrac{\text{kg} \cdot \text{m} \cdot \text{s}}{\text{s}^2 \cdot \text{m}^2}\right)\left(\text{m}^3\right)}$ (dimensionless)

THE CORRECT ANSWER IS: C

63. The cross-sectional area of the pipe is:

$$A_c = \frac{\pi}{4} D^2 = \frac{\pi}{4}(0.10)^2 = 0.007854 \text{ m}^2$$

The flow rate is:

$$Q = A_c V_c = 0.007854 \ (2.5)(60) = 1.178 \text{ m}^3/\text{min}$$

THE CORRECT ANSWER IS: B

FE MECHANICAL SOLUTIONS

64. Refer to the pump power equation in the Fluid Mechanics chapter of the *FE Reference Handbook.*

$$\dot{W} = \frac{Q\gamma h}{\eta} = \frac{\Delta P \cdot Q}{\eta} \qquad \text{since } \Delta P = \gamma h$$

$$\eta = \frac{\Delta P \cdot Q}{\dot{W}} = \frac{(0.9 \text{ kPa})(3.0 \text{ m}^3/\text{s})}{4.0 \text{ kW}} \cdot \frac{\text{kN}}{\text{m}^2 \cdot \text{kPa}} \cdot \frac{\text{kW} \cdot \text{s}}{\text{kN} \cdot \text{m}}$$

$$= 0.675$$

THE CORRECT ANSWER IS: C

65. Refer to the Thermodynamics section of the *FE Reference Handbook*. Use the ideal gas formula:

$$PV = mRT$$

$$P = \frac{mRT}{V}$$

$$R = \frac{8{,}314 \text{ J}}{\text{kmole} \cdot \text{K}} \frac{\text{kmol}}{28 \text{ kg}} = 297 \frac{\text{J}}{\text{kg} \cdot \text{K}}$$

$$P = \frac{(100 \text{ kg}) \left(297 \dfrac{\text{J}}{\text{kg} \cdot \text{K}} \right) (343 \text{ K})}{100 \text{ m}^3}$$

$$= 102{,}000 \frac{\text{J}}{\text{m}^3}$$

$$= 102{,}000 \frac{\text{N} \cdot \text{m}}{\text{m}^3}$$

$$= 102{,}000 \frac{\text{N}}{\text{m}^2}$$

$$= 102 \text{ kPa}$$

THE CORRECT ANSWER IS: B

FE MECHANICAL SOLUTIONS

66. As vapor escapes, the mass within the tank is reduced. With constant volume, the specific volume within the tank must increase. This can happen only if liquid evaporates.

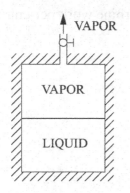

THE CORRECT ANSWER IS: A

67. The specific volume is found using the ideal gas equation of state.

$$pv = RT$$

$$v = \left(\frac{RT}{p}\right) = \frac{[0.287 \text{ kJ/(kg·K)}][273 + 100]\text{ K}}{172 \text{ kPa}}$$

Unit check

$$v = 0.622 \text{ m}^3/\text{kg} \qquad \frac{\dfrac{\text{kJ}}{\text{kg·K}} \times \text{K}}{\dfrac{\text{kN}}{\text{m}^2}} = \frac{\text{kN·m·K·m}^3}{\text{kg·K·kN}} = \frac{\text{m}^3}{\text{kg}}$$

THE CORRECT ANSWER IS: B

FE MECHANICAL SOLUTIONS

68. Assuming steady-state, steady-flow conditions, a first law analysis of the turbine yields,

$$w_t = h_4 - h_3$$

and with the enthalpy values provided for States 3 and 4, the turbine work per unit mass is

$$w_t = 3,478.5 - 2,584.7 = 893.8 \text{ kJ/kg}$$

The power produced by the turbine is given by

$$\dot{W} = \dot{m}w_t = (50 \text{ kg/s})(893.8 \text{ kJ/kg}) = 44,690 \text{ kW} = 44.7 \text{ MW}$$

THE CORRECT ANSWER IS: B

69. An energy balance on the boiler gives:

$$\dot{Q} = \dot{m}(h_2 - h_1) = \left(\frac{50,000 \text{ kg}}{3,600 \text{ s}}\right)\left[(3,322 - 167.6) \text{ kJ/kg}\right] = 43,811 \text{ kW} = 44 \text{ MW}$$

THE CORRECT ANSWER IS: D

70. Flow through an insulated valve closely follows a throttling process. A throttling process is at constant enthalpy.

THE CORRECT ANSWERS ARE: B and E

71. The isentropic efficiency for a pump is $\eta_p = \dfrac{w_s}{w_{actual}}$

The isentropic pump work for a constant density fluid is

$$w_s = v\Delta P = (0.001010 \text{ m}^3/\text{kg})(1,000 \text{ kPa} - 10 \text{ kPa}) = 0.9999 \text{ kJ/kg}$$

and the actual power required at the pump is

$$\dot{W}_a = \dot{m}w_s / \eta_p = (50 \text{ kg/s})(0.9999 \text{ kJ/kg}) / 0.7 = 71 \text{ kW}$$

THE CORRECT ANSWER IS: D

FE MECHANICAL SOLUTIONS

72. Refer to the First Law of Thermodynamics section, the Common Thermodynamic Cycles section, and the P-h diagram for Refrigerant HFC-134a in the Thermodynamics chapter of the *FE Reference Handbook*.

The coefficient of performance of a refrigeration cycle (COP) is defined as the heat added to the refrigerant in the evaporator divided by the work put into the compressor. The heat added, per unit mass of refrigerant, is given by the First Law of Thermodynamics.

$$\dot{m}\left(h_i + \frac{\cancel{v_i^2}^{0}}{2} + \cancel{gz_i}^{0}\right) - \dot{m}\left(h_e + \frac{\cancel{v_e^2}^{0}}{2} \cancel{gz_e}^{0}\right) + \dot{Q}_{net} - \cancel{\dot{W}_{net}}^{0} = 0$$

thus $\dot{Q}_{net} = \dot{m}(h_e - h_i) = \dot{m}(h_1 - h_4)$

The work is found similarly, with $\dot{Q}_{net} = 0$, giving $W_{net} = \dot{m}(h_i - h_e) = \dot{m}(h_1 - h_2)$.

This gives $\text{COP} = \dfrac{\dot{Q}_{in}}{-\dot{W}_{net}} = \dfrac{\dot{m}(h_1 - h_4)}{\dot{m}(h_1 - h_2)}$

From the P-h diagram

$h_1 = 394\dfrac{kJ}{kg}$, $h_2 = 438\dfrac{kJ}{kg}$, and $h_4 = 270\dfrac{kJ}{kg}$

$\text{COP} = \dfrac{(h_1 - h_4)}{(h_2 - h_1)} = \dfrac{394 - 270}{438 - 394} = 2.82$

Note that the expansion from h_3 and h_4 is assumed to be constant enthalpy. Therefore, $h_3 = h_4$.

THE CORRECT ANSWER IS: B

73. From the P-h Diagram for Refrigerant HFC-134a given in the Thermodynamics section of the *FE Reference Handbook*:

$h_1 = 400 \text{ kJ/kg}$

$h_3 = h_4 = 257 \text{ kJ/kg}$

Evaporator cooling is $q_{41} = h_1 - h_4 = 400\dfrac{kJ}{kg} - 257\dfrac{kJ}{kg} = 143\dfrac{kJ}{kg}$

THE CORRECT ANSWER IS: B

FE MECHANICAL SOLUTIONS

74. From the *P-h* Diagram for Refrigerant HFC-134a given in the Thermodynamics section of the *FE Reference Handbook*:

$$h_1 = 400 \text{ kJ/kg}$$
$$h_2 = 425 \text{ kJ/kg}$$
$$h_3 = h_4 = 257 \text{ kJ/kg}$$

The process from 3 to 4 is a throttling process, which involves both a drop in pressure and temperature. It is an irreversible process, generally considered constant enthalpy.

THE CORRECT ANSWER IS: B

75. Refer to the psychrometric chart in the Thermodynamics chapter of the *FE Reference Handbook*.

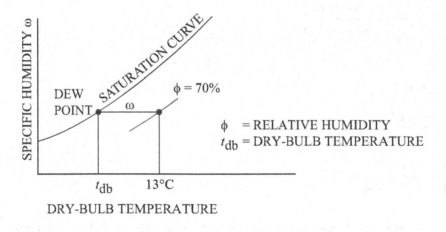

At the given state, $t_{db} = 13°C$, $\phi = 70\%$, $\omega = 6.5 \dfrac{\text{g}}{\text{kg da}}$, da = dry air.

Follow the $\omega = 6.5$ line to the left until the saturation curve is reached. This point is the dew point. Read down to find the dew-point temperature of $7.6°C$.

THE CORRECT ANSWER IS: B

FE MECHANICAL SOLUTIONS

76. Refer to the Thermodynamics section of the *FE Reference Handbook*.

The definition of *relative humidity*:

$$\phi = \frac{p_v}{p_g} = \frac{\text{vapor pressure}}{\text{saturation pressure}}$$

THE CORRECT ANSWER IS: A

77. Refer to the Heat Transfer section of the *FE Reference Handbook*.

$$\dot{Q} = hA\Delta T$$

$$\dot{Q} = 72(2)(150)$$

$$\dot{Q} = 21,600 \text{ W}$$

THE CORRECT ANSWER IS: D

78.
$$\text{Re} = \frac{v(2r_i)P}{\mu}$$

$$= \frac{6 \text{ m/s}(2 \cdot 0.050 \text{ m})\left(10.844 \text{ kg/m}^3\right)}{2.0417 \times 10^{-5} \text{ kg/m} \cdot \text{s}}$$

$$= 318,681$$

$$h_i = 0.027 \frac{k_f}{2r_i} \text{Re}^{0.8} \text{Pr}^{1/3} \left(\frac{\mu_b}{\mu_s}\right)^{0.14}$$

$$= 0.027 \left(\frac{0.0245 \text{ kJ/m} \cdot \text{K}}{2 \cdot 0.050 \text{ m}}\right)(318,681)^{0.8} (1.12)^{1/3} (1)^{0.14}$$

$$= 173.6 \text{ W/m}^2 \cdot \text{K}$$

THE CORRECT ANSWER IS: B

FE MECHANICAL SOLUTIONS

79. Refer to the Shape Factor Relations section in the Heat Transfer chapter of the *FE Reference Handbook*.

Consider the figure shown. The ground plane A_3 is moved downward to location A_3' so that A_1 is halfway between A_2 and A_3'. The shape factor F_{12} is the fraction of all the rays leaving A_1 that arrive at A_2. By symmetry, half the rays leaving A_1 strike A_2 and half strike A_3'.

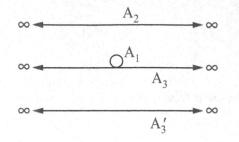

Now the shape factor F_{13} is the same as F_{13}' because each ray that leaves A_1 and strikes A_3' must cross A_3, and each ray that leaves A_1 and strikes A_3 will, if extended, also strike A_3'.

Then by the equations in the Shape Factor Relations section:

$F_{11} + F_{12} + F_{13} = 1$ but $F_{11} = 0$ since Surface A_1 cannot "see" itself

$F_{12} = F_{13}$

Thus $F_{12} + F_{12} = 1$

$F_{12} = \dfrac{1}{2}$

THE CORRECT ANSWER IS: B

80.
$$Q_{1-2} = \sigma A_1 F_{1-2} \left(T_1^4 - T_2^4 \right)$$
$$= 5.67 \times 10^{-8} \, (4)(0.275)\left(773^4 - 673^4 \right)$$
$$= 9474 = 9.47 \, \text{kW}$$

THE CORRECT ANSWER IS: B

FE MECHANICAL SOLUTIONS

81. Refer to the Heating and Cooling Loads section in the Mechanical Engineering chapter of the *FE Reference Handbook*.

$$R'' = \frac{1}{h_i} + \frac{L_{cs}}{k_{cs}} + \frac{L_{AL}}{k_{AL}} + \frac{1}{h_\infty}$$

$$R'' = \frac{1}{700 \text{ W/m}^2 \cdot \text{K}} + \frac{0.01 \text{ m}}{60 \text{ W/m} \cdot \text{K}} + \frac{0.01 \text{ m}}{240 \text{ W/m} \cdot \text{K}} + \frac{1}{100 \text{ W/m}^2 \cdot \text{K}}$$

$$R'' = 0.01164 \frac{\text{m}^2 \cdot \text{K}}{\text{W}}$$

$$U = \frac{1}{R''} = \frac{1}{0.01164 \frac{\text{m}^2 \cdot \text{K}}{\text{W}}} = 85.93 \frac{\text{W}}{\text{m}^2 \cdot \text{K}}$$

$$\dot{Q} = UA(T_i - T_o)$$

$$\frac{\dot{Q}}{A} = U(T_i - T_o)$$

$$\frac{\dot{Q}}{A} = \left(85.93 \frac{\text{W}}{\text{m}^2 \cdot \text{K}}\right)(544 \text{ K} - 300 \text{ K})$$

$$\frac{\dot{Q}}{A} = 20,968 \text{ W} / \text{m}^2$$

THE CORRECT ANSWER IS: C

FE MECHANICAL SOLUTIONS

82. Find: Temperatures of the steel and aluminum plate surfaces and the interior temperature between the aluminum and steel plates. Compare to determine the smallest temperature difference.

Approach:

1. Determine the heat transfer rate ($\dot{Q}$).

$\dot{Q} = A(T_i - T_\infty)/R''$ (refer to the Heating and Cooling Loads section in the Mechanical Engineering chapter of the *FE Reference Handbook*).

$A = (1\,\text{m})(1\,\text{m}) = 1\,\text{m}^2$

$T_i = 544\,\text{K}$

$T_\infty = 300\,\text{K}$

$R'' = \dfrac{1}{h_i} + \dfrac{L_s}{k_S} + \dfrac{L_A}{k_A} + \dfrac{1}{h_\infty}$

$R'' = \dfrac{1}{700\,(\text{W/m}^2\cdot\text{K})} + \dfrac{0.01\,\text{m}}{60\,\text{W/(m·K)}} + \dfrac{0.01\,\text{m}}{240\,\text{W/(m·K)}} + \dfrac{1}{100\,(\text{W/m}^2\cdot\text{K})}$

$= 0.01164\,\dfrac{\text{K·m}^2}{\text{W}}$

Substitute and solve for $\dot{Q}$

$\dot{Q} = \dfrac{(1\,\text{m}^2)(544\,\text{K} - 300\,\text{K})}{0.01164\,\dfrac{\text{K·m}^2}{\text{W}}}$

$\dot{Q} = 20{,}970\,\text{W}$

82. **(Continued)**

2. Determine $T_{S,A}$.

$$\dot{Q} = \frac{A(T_i - T_{S,A})}{R''_{i \to S,A}}$$

$$T_{S,A} = T_i - \frac{\dot{Q}\,R''_{i \to S,A}}{A}$$

$$R''_{i \to S,A} = \frac{1}{700\left(\mathrm{W/m^2 \cdot K}\right)} + \frac{0.01\ \mathrm{m}}{60\ \mathrm{W/(m \cdot K)}} = 0.001596\,\frac{\mathrm{m^2 \cdot K}}{\mathrm{W}}$$

$$T_{S,A} = 544 - \frac{(20{,}970\ \mathrm{W})\left(0.001596\dfrac{\mathrm{m^2 \cdot K}}{\mathrm{W}}\right)}{1\ \mathrm{m^2}}$$

$$T_{S,A} = 510.5\ \mathrm{K}$$

THE CORRECT ANSWER IS: C

83. The effect of fouling on the heat-transfer surfaces is to reduce the heat-transfer rate by increasing the surface resistance. The results on the water being heated would be to reduce the outlet temperature of the water.

THE CORRECT ANSWER IS: B

FE MECHANICAL SOLUTIONS

84. Subscript H indicates hot fluid.
Subscript C indicates cold fluid.

$$\dot{Q} = \dot{m}_H c_{P,H}(T_{H_{in}} - T_{H_{out}})$$
$$= \dot{m}_C c_{P,C}(T_{C_{out}} - T_{C_{in}})$$

Water is the cold fluid, so:

$$\dot{m}_C = \dot{m}_H \frac{c_{P,H}}{c_{P,C}}\left(\frac{\Delta T_H}{\Delta T_C}\right)$$

$$= (2.25 \text{ kg/s})\left(\frac{3.5}{4.186}\right)\left(\frac{204-79}{79-29}\right)$$

$$= (2.25)(0.836)\left(\frac{125}{50}\right)$$

$$= 4.70$$

THE CORRECT ANSWER IS: B

85. $$\Delta T_{lm} = \frac{\left(T_{H_o} - T_{C_i}\right) - \left(T_{H_i} - T_{C_o}\right)}{\ln\left(\dfrac{T_{H_o} - T_{C_i}}{T_{H_i} - T_{C_o}}\right)} \text{ for counterflow HE}$$

$$\Delta T_{lm} = \frac{(65°C - 24°C) - (110°C - 60°C)}{\ln\left(\dfrac{65°C - 24°C}{110°C - 60°C}\right)}$$

$$\Delta T_{lm} = 45.4°C$$

THE CORRECT ANSWER IS: C

FE MECHANICAL SOLUTIONS

86. The overall heat-transfer coefficient based on inside surface area is found from the shell-and-tube heat exchanger equation in the Heat Transfer section of the *FE Reference Handbook.*

$$\frac{1}{UA} = \frac{1}{h_i A_i} + \frac{R_{f(i)}}{A_i} + \frac{\ln\left(\dfrac{D_o}{D_i}\right)}{2\pi kL} + \frac{R_{f(o)}}{A_o} + \frac{1}{h_o A_o}$$

If $A = A_i$

$$\frac{1}{U} = \frac{1}{h_i} + R_{f(i)} + \frac{A_i \ln\left(\dfrac{D_o}{D_i}\right)}{2\pi kL} + \frac{A_i}{A_o}R_{f(o)} + \frac{A_i}{h_o A_o}$$

$h_i = 6,000$

$R_{f(i)} = 7 \times 10^{-4}$

$k = 380$

$$\frac{A_i \ln\left(\dfrac{D_o}{D_i}\right)}{2\pi kL} = \frac{(\pi D_i L)\ln\left(\dfrac{D_o}{D_i}\right)}{2\pi kL} = \frac{D_i \ln\left(\dfrac{D_o}{D_i}\right)}{2k}$$

$R_{f(o)} = 9 \times 10^{-5}$

$h_o = 12,000$

$$\frac{A_i}{A_o} = \frac{\pi D_i L}{\pi D_o L} = \frac{D_i}{D_o} = \frac{2.5 \times 10^{-2}}{3.8 \times 10^{-2}}$$

$$\frac{1}{U} = \frac{1}{6,000} + 7 \times 10^{-4} + \frac{(2.5 \times 10^{-2})\ln\dfrac{(3.8 \times 10^{-2})}{(2.5 \times 10^{-2})}}{2(380)} + \frac{2.5}{3.8}\left(9 \times 10^{-5}\right) + \frac{2.5}{(3.8)(12,000)}$$

$$\frac{1}{U} = 1.667 \times 10^{-4} + 7 \times 10^{-4} + 0.138 \times 10^{-4} + 0.592 \times 10^{-4} + 0.548 \times 10^{-4}$$

$$\frac{1}{U} = 9.945 \times 10^{-4}$$

$$U = 1,005.5 \text{ W/(m}^2 \cdot \text{K)}$$

THE CORRECT ANSWER IS: A

87. $R = R_o\,[1 + \alpha(T - T_o)]$

$\Delta R = \dfrac{dR}{dT}\,\Delta T$

$\quad\quad = R_o\alpha\Delta T$

$\quad\quad = (100\ \Omega)\,(0.004°C^{-1})\,(10°C)$

$\quad\quad = 4.0\ \Omega$

THE CORRECT ANSWER IS: C

88.   The solution requires a step-by-step reduction of the system loops.

First, reduce the inner loop.

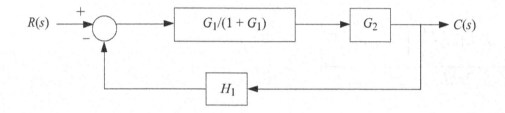

Next, combine the forward blocks.

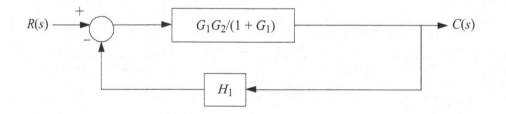

Finally, reduce the outer loop.

$$R(s) \longrightarrow \boxed{(G_1G_2)/(1 + G_1 + G_1G_2H_1)} \longrightarrow C(s)$$

THE CORRECT ANSWER IS: D

89. Rewriting the temperature equation

$$\frac{T(t) - T_o}{T_i - T_o} = e^{-t/\tau}$$

For $T(t) = 139°C$,

$$\frac{139 - 140}{40 - 140} = e^{-t/3}$$

or $\quad t = 3 \ln 100 = 13.8 \text{ sec}$

THE CORRECT ANSWER IS: D

90. Refer to the Control Systems section in the Measurement and Controls chapter of the *FE Reference Handbook* to complete the Routh Array shown.

Routh Array

1	200
54	200 K
b_1	0
c_1	

$$b_1 = \frac{(54)(200) - (1)(200\text{ K})}{54}$$

$$= \frac{10,800 - 200\text{ K}}{54}$$

$$c_1 = 200\,K$$

For stability :

$$c_1 \geq 0 \quad \Rightarrow \quad K \geq 0$$

$$b_1 \geq 0 \quad \Rightarrow \quad K \leq 54$$

Hence, $K_{\max} = 54$

THE CORRECT ANSWER IS: D

91. The equation of the system can be written as $\dfrac{16}{s\left(s^2 + 0.8s + 16\right)}$ which is in the form

$$\dfrac{16}{s\left(s^2 + 2\zeta\omega_n\, s + \omega_n^2\right)}$$

thus $\omega_n^2 = 16$ or $\omega_n = 4$

and $2\zeta\omega_n = 0.8$ or $\zeta = \dfrac{0.8}{2\omega_n} = 0.1$

THE CORRECT ANSWER IS: C

92. Since $U_{To} = U_\alpha = U_{Ro} \equiv 0$

$$U_R^2 = \left[\left(\dfrac{\partial R}{\partial T}\right)U_T\right]^2$$

Also, $\dfrac{\partial R}{\partial T} = R_o\alpha$

so $U_R = 0.1 = (R_o\alpha)U_T$

$$= [100 \times (0.3925 \times 10^{-3})]U_T$$

and $U_T = 2.55°C$

THE CORRECT ANSWER IS: D

93. Maximum bending $= 900\ \text{mm} \times 1{,}200\ \text{N} = 1.08 \times 10^6\ \text{N·mm}$

$$\sigma_{tension} = \dfrac{\left(1.08 \times 10^6\ \text{N·mm}\right)(15\ \text{mm})}{11 \times 10^4\ \text{mm}^4} = 147\ \text{MPa}$$

THE CORRECT ANSWER IS: B

94.

$$\sigma_{max} = \frac{Mc}{I} = \frac{PL\left(\frac{h}{2}\right)}{\frac{1}{12}bh^3}$$

where **P** = 40 N
   h = 10 mm
   b = 20 mm
and L = 800 mm

This gives σ_{max} = 96 MPa

Since the min stress = 0 (no load)

$\sigma_{min} = 0$

$$\therefore \quad \sigma_a = \frac{96-0}{2} = 48 \text{ MPa}$$

$$\sigma_m = \frac{96+0}{2} = 48 \text{ MPa}$$

and $\dfrac{48}{200} + \dfrac{48}{300} = \dfrac{1}{n} = 0.4$

$\therefore$ n = 2.50

THE CORRECT ANSWER IS: D

95. Refer to the Mechanical Springs section in the Mechanical Engineering chapter of the *FE Reference Handbook.*

$$\tau = K_s \frac{8FD}{\pi d^3}$$

where

$d = 2.34$ mm

$d_o = 15$ mm

$D = d_o - d = 15 - 2.34 = 12.66$ mm

$C = \dfrac{D}{d} = \dfrac{12.66}{2.34} = 5.410$

$K_s = \dfrac{2C+1}{2C} = \dfrac{2(5.410)+1}{2(5.410)} = 1.0924$

$$\tau = 1.0924 \frac{(8)(150\ \text{N})(12.66\ \text{mm})}{\pi(2.34)^3} = 412.3\ \text{MPa}$$

THE CORRECT ANSWER IS: C

96. The force required to displace a spring an amount δ from its free length is $F = k\delta$, where k is the spring constant or rate. In this case:

δ = free length – compressed length

= 190 mm – 125 mm

= 65 mm

The force required to deflect the spring this amount is:

$F = k\delta = (38.525\ \text{N/mm})(65\ \text{mm}) = 2{,}504\ \text{N}$

THE CORRECT ANSWER IS: B

97. Refer to Cylindrical Pressure Vessel in the Mechanics of Materials section of the *FE Reference Handbook*.

The cylinder can be considered thin-walled if $t < d_o/20$. In this case, $t = 12$ mm and $r_o = d_o/2 = 362$ mm. Thus

$$\sigma_t = \frac{P_i r}{t}$$

where $r = \dfrac{r_i + r_o}{2} = \dfrac{350 + 362}{2} = 356$ mm

$$\sigma_t = \frac{(1.680\ \text{MPa})(356\ \text{mm})}{12\ \text{mm}} = 49.8\ \text{MPa}$$

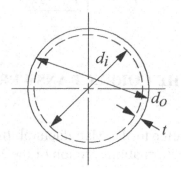

THE CORRECT ANSWER IS: B

98. The formula for the total longitudinal strain without a temperature rise is:

$$\varepsilon_{\text{axial}} = \frac{1}{E}\left(\sigma_l - v\left(\sigma_t + \sigma_r\right)\right) = \frac{1}{210 \times 10^3\ \text{MPa}}\left(23.1\ \text{MPa} - 0.24\left(46.2\ \text{MPa} + 0\right)\right) = 5.72 \times 10^{-6}$$

This must be converted to displacement using the following formula:

$$\varepsilon_{\text{axial}} = \frac{\delta l}{l}, \text{where } l \text{ is the length of the section under consideration}$$

$$\delta l = \varepsilon_{\text{axial}} \times l$$

$$= 5.72 \times 10^{-6} \times 1{,}000\ \text{mm}$$

$$= 0.0572\ \text{mm}$$

THE CORRECT ANSWER IS: A

FE MECHANICAL SOLUTIONS

99. The formula for the hoop stress is:

$$\sigma_t = \frac{P_i \times r_m}{t} = \frac{P_i\left(\dfrac{D_o + D_i}{4}\right)}{\left(\dfrac{D_o - D_i}{2}\right)} = 0.6\ \text{MPa} \times \frac{306.25\ \text{mm}}{2.5\ \text{mm}} = 73.5\ \text{MPa}$$

THE CORRECT ANSWER IS: C

100. Refer to the Manufacturability section in the Mechanical Engineering chapter and the Thermal Deformations section of the Mechanics of Materials chapter of the *FE Reference Handbook*.

Required diameter change:

$$\delta_{\text{diameter}} = d_{\text{shaft}} - d_{\text{pulley}} + \text{required assembly clearance}$$
$$= 100.15 - 100.00 + 0.05 = 0.20\ \text{mm}$$

Required temperature change of pulley diameter:

$$\delta_{\text{diameter}} = \alpha\, d(\Delta T)$$

$$\Delta T = \frac{\delta_{\text{diameter}}}{\alpha\, d} = \frac{0.20}{(11 \times 10^{-6})(100)} = 181.8°\text{C}$$

Temperature to which pulley must be heated:

$$T = T_{\text{room}} + \Delta T = 20 + 182 = 202°\text{C}$$

THE CORRECT ANSWER IS: D

FE EXAM PREPARATION MATERIAL
PUBLISHED BY NCEES

FE Reference Handbook

FE Practice Exams for all modules:
Chemical
Civil
Electrical and Computer
Environmental
Industrial and Systems
Mechanical
Other Disciplines

For more information about these and other NCEES publications and services,
visit us at www.ncees.org or contact
Client Services at (800) 250-3196.